MYTHS, FABLES, AND FOLKTALES

MYTHS, FABLES, AND FOLKTALES

ALBERT R. KITZHABER
General Editor

STODDARD MALARKEY
Literature Editor

HOLT, RINEHART AND WINSTON, INC.
New York • Toronto • London • Sydney

ISBN: 0-03-010891-8

3456 071 1098

This text comprises the sections "Fables, Parables, and Proverbs," "Mythology," and "Folktales" from *Elements in Literature*, copyright © 1974 by Holt, Rinehart and Winston, Inc.

Illustration credits appear in the back on page v.

ACKNOWLEDGMENTS

The authors and publisher have made every effort to trace the ownership of all selections found in this book and to make full acknowledgment for their use. Many of the selections are in the public domain. Grateful acknowledgment is made to the following authors, publishers, agents, and individuals for their permission to reprint copyrighted material.

THE HERITAGE PRESS, INC., for "The Ant and the Grasshopper" and "The Lion and the Mouse" from Munro Leaf's version of *Aesop's Fables*. Copyright 1941 by The Heritage Press, Inc. Reprinted by permission.

G. P. PUTNAM'S SONS, for "The Two Elephants," "The Dog and the Wolf," "The Elephant in Favor," and "The Fox and the Grapes" from *Various Fables from Various Places*, edited by Diane di Prima. Copyright © 1960 by G. P. Putnam's Sons. Reprinted by permission.

MRS. HELEN THURBER and HAMISH HAMILTON LTD., for "The Birds and the Foxes" from *Fables For Our Time* by James Thurber. Copyright 1940 by James Thurber and published by Harper & Row, Inc. Originally appeared in *The New Yorker*. Reprinted by permission.

COLLINS-KNOWLTON-WING, INC., MR. ROBERT GRAVES, CASSELL & CO. LTD., and A. P. WATT & SON, for "Orpheus," "Daedalus," "Bellerophon," "The Labors of Heracles," and "Perseus" from *Greek Gods and Heroes (Myths of Ancient Greece for Children)*. Copyright © 1960 by Robert Graves. Reprinted by permission.

HOUGHTON MIFFLIN COMPANY, INC., for "The Creation," "Hymer's Caldron," "Thor and the Giant King," "The Fenris Wolf," and "Baldur, the Beautiful" from *Legends of the North* by Olivia E. Coolidge. Copyright 1951 by Olivia E. Coolidge. Reprinted by permission.

HARCOURT BRACE JOVANOVICH, INC., for "The Story of Creation" from *The African Saga* by Blaise Cendrars. Reprinted by permission.

HENRY Z. WALCK, INC. and OXFORD UNIVERSITY PRESS, for "Thunder and Lightning" and "Why the Bush-Fowl Calls at Dawn and Why Flies Buzz" from *African Myths and Legends* by Kathleen Arnott. Copyright © 1962 by Kathleen Arnott. Reprinted by permission.

THE VIKING PRESS, for "How the People Sang the Mountain Up" and "Why the Bat Flies Alone" from *How the People Sang the Mountain Up* by Maria Leach. Copyright © 1967 by Maria Leach. Reprinted by permission.

INTRODUCTION

Peoples all over the world share many of the same concerns, problems, hopes, and dreams. Often these common concerns become the basis for folk literature.

The heritage of folk literature is passed on from generation to generation, often without being written down. This is an oral heritage, developed by storytellers over the years, each one adding new details or characters.

The myths, fables, and folktales collected in this book come from many parts of the world—ancient Greece and Scandinavia, Africa, and the Indians of North America. Yet all of them are part of our cultural heritage because they deal with the basic concerns of human life.

Contents

Contents

Fables,
Parables,
and Proverbs

Just as human experience is made up of things and ideas, so the subject of a work of literature can be about things and ideas. Things are concrete: you can see, hear, touch, taste, or smell them. Ideas are abstract: they can be felt, but they can't be reached by any of the five senses. In the same way, we can call the subject of a work *concrete* or *abstract*. What is actually happening in a story or poem is its *concrete* subject; the idea the author is trying to get across is its *abstract* subject.

In this unit and those that follow it, you are going to see how this combination of concrete and abstract works in such storied forms as fables, parables, myths, and folktales. You probably already know some of these stories, but you will also

1

have a chance to read other and more unfamiliar stories from other countries. Many things about the form of these stories, as well as their subjects, will certainly be new and interesting.

Fables

We begin with a fable you may already know. If you don't, you are about to learn where the expression "sour grapes" comes from.

The Fox and The Grapes

Aesop

One hot summer's day, a Fox was strolling through an orchard when he came upon a bunch of Grapes which had just turned ripe on a vine that was growing over a lofty branch. "Just the thing to quench my thirst," he thought. Drawing back a few paces, he took a run and a jump and just missed the bunch. Turning round, he again essayed the jump, but with no better success. Again and again he tried after the tempting morsel, but at last had to give it up and walked away with his nose in the air, saying to himself,

"I am sure they are sour."

DON'T SNEER AT SOMETHING JUST BECAUSE YOU CAN'T HAVE IT.

QUESTIONS FOR DISCUSSION

1. Why do you think the fox said the grapes were sour? Were they? Whom was he trying to convince?
2. What defect of character does the fox demonstrate? Would you normally expect this behavior from foxes? If not, what creature does act like this?
3. What part of the fable is the concrete subject? What part is the abstract subject?

4. The phrase "sour grapes" is an *allusion* to this fable. Make sure you understand the meaning of the term *allusion*, and then discuss in class the kinds of situations in which this particular allusion might be used.

Understanding Words

What do you think the word *essayed* means in this context? It also means "to put to a test."

You have probably come across the word *essay* used as a noun. What is an *essay?* What is the person called who writes essays?

Most of the fables you know or will hear of are from a collection usually called *Aesop's Fables.* Aesop was a slave in ancient Greece, famous for telling fables. The story goes, however, that he told one fable too many —a fable whose moral criticized the character of his master. So his master had him killed. Perhaps Aesop's death, and the cause of it, would make a good fable itself! Here is one of the most popular of all Aesop's fables.

Antonio Frasconi, 1954

The Hare and the Tortoise

Aesop

A hare jeered at a tortoise for the slowness of his pace. But he laughed and said, that he would run against her and beat her any day she should name. "Come on," said the hare, "you shall soon see what my feet are made of." So it was agreed that they should start at once. The tortoise went off jogging along, without a moment's stopping, at his usual steady pace. The hare, treating the whole matter very lightly, said she would first take a little nap, and that she should soon overtake the tortoise. Meanwhile the tortoise plodded on, and the hare oversleeping herself, arrived at the goal, only to see that the tortoise had got in before her.

SLOW AND STEADY WINS THE RACE.

QUESTIONS FOR DISCUSSION

1. What defect in character does the hare, or rabbit, demonstrate? Do you normally expect this behavior in rabbits? If not, what creature does act like this?
2. What part of the fable is the concrete subject? What part is the abstract subject? Based on this fable and the first one, can you make any statement about the pattern fables seem to follow?

Fables, Parables, and Proverbs

4

Aesop may have talked too much for his own health, but he was usually pretty clever. The story goes that one day his master wished to take a long day's trip to another palace. Aesop, being lame, was granted first choice of the loads to be carried. He chose the heaviest load, the baskets of food for the trip. Everyone laughed at him. When they stopped for lunch, however, Aesop's load was lightened by half. When they stopped for an early dinner, Aesop's baskets were emptied. At the end of the day's weary journey, when the other men were still groaning under loads of luggage, Aesop was strolling along with nothing but empty baskets. Can you think of a proverb about laughing which fits the story? The two fables that follow may teach you something about thinking ahead.

The Ant and the Grasshopper

Munro Leaf's version of Aesop's fable

In the early winter, a whole colony of Ants were out working hard, turning over in the sun the food they had gathered all summer, so that it wouldn't spoil.

While they were busy at this, along came a bedraggled Grasshopper who had managed somehow to live after the summer. He was cold and thin and very hungry. So he went up to one of the Ants and said in a whiny voice, "How about giving me a little bit of all that food you have there, Ant?"

"I am sorry, Grasshopper, but we worked all summer to gather this food and we need every bit of it to feed us through the winter. What did you do all summer?"

"Oh, I sang and drank and danced all the time. I couldn't bother to work. Why, what does that have to do with it? I'm hungry now, not last summer."

"That is just the point," said the Ant. "If we sang and danced and drank all summer we would starve in the winter and it looks as though that is what you are going to do. Goodbye," and he went on with his work.

SAVE WHILE YOU ARE YOUNG OR
YOU'LL HAVE NOTHING WHEN YOU ARE OLD

Understanding Words

An Interesting Word

Used as a verb, *bedraggle* means "to wet thoroughly." *Bedraggled* is usually used as an adjective, however, as it is here, and it has come to mean "dilapidated," because one looks that way after being wet and dragged through mud and dirt. The *be* prefix begins quite a few adjectives ending in *ed*: *bewhiskered*, *befriended*, and *bedecked* are examples. Can you think of any others?

The Lion and the Mouse

Munro Leaf's version of Aesop's fable

A Lion, who was hot and tired from hunting, lay down under a big shady oak tree. When he fell asleep a company of little mice played around and over him. The Lion woke with a start and slapped his big paw down on one of them and held him fast.

"Please don't kill me, Lion," squeaked the Mouse. "I didn't mean any harm and if you will let me go I'll help you out sometime."

"Haw! haw!" laughed the Lion, "a little smidge like you help me! That *is* funny." But the Lion wasn't really mean and he felt quite happy, so he let the Mouse go.

Not long after that the Lion ran into a big net that some hunters had set to catch him. He let out a roar that shook the forest all around. The Mouse heard him and thought he recognized the voice of his friend, so he went over to see what had happened.

There was the Lion all tangled up in the rope net, just about ready to give up and wait for the hunters to come and kill him.

"Well, Lion, even you are in a fix this time," said the Mouse, and with his sharp little teeth he gnawed the net apart until the Lion could crawl out and run free.

KINDNESS IS A GOOD THING FOR ALL OF US TO
PRACTICE, NO MATTER HOW BIG OR SMALL WE ARE.

QUESTION FOR DISCUSSION

*Fables, Parables,
and Proverbs*

6

You have now read four of Aesop's fables. They all involved animals. Is the subject of a fable usually about animal behavior? If not, what is it about? Can you make a general statement about the purpose of fables?

In view of the fact that Aesop was a slave, what do you think his feelings were when he told this fable?

The Dog and the Wolf
Aesop

A gaunt Wolf was almost dead with hunger when he happened to meet a House-dog who was passing by. "Ah, Cousin," said the Dog, "I knew how it would be; your irregular life will soon be the ruin of you. Why do you not work steadily as I do, and get your food regularly given to you?"

"I would have no objection," said the Wolf, "if I could only get a place."

"I will easily arrange that for you," said the Dog. "Come with me to my master and you shall share my work."

So the Wolf and the Dog went towards the town together. On the way there the Wolf noticed that the hair on a certain part of the Dog's neck was very much worn away, so he asked him how that had come about.

"Oh, it is nothing," said the Dog. "That is only the place where the collar is put on at night to keep me chained up; it chafes a bit, but one soon gets used to it."

"Is that all?" said the Wolf. "Then goodbye to you, Master Dog. I would rather starve free than be a fat slave."

QUESTIONS FOR DISCUSSION

1. This fable has no moral following it. Try to work out a moral for it in class. Be sure that it is short and to the point: a moral is no good if it is too long or not clear.
2. The fables you have read are usually called *beast fables*. Why? Can you work out in class a definition of the beast fable which includes all the common characteristics of this literary form?

Understanding Words

Context Clues

Sometimes a writer explains a word he uses by giving a definition of it in the same sentence. What do you think the word *gaunt* means in the first sentence, considering that the author tells you the wolf was almost dead with hunger?

Aesop did not make up all of his fables. In fact, he probably made up very few of them. Fables are found in all countries among all peoples. They are apparently very ancient and existed long before the invention of writing. They are part of the *oral tradition* of a people, in the same way that the traditional ballad is. Here are a few fables from other lands.

The Elephant in Favor

Ivan Krilof

Once upon a time, the Elephant stood high in the good graces of the Lion. The forest immediately began to talk about the matter, and, as usual, many guesses were made as to the means by which the Elephant had gained such favor.

"It is no beauty," say the beasts to each other, "and it is not amusing. And what habits it has! What manners!"

Says the Fox, whisking about his brush, "If it had possessed such a bushy tail as mine, I should not have wondered."

"Or, sister," says the Bear, "if it had got into favor on account of claws, no one would have found the matter at all extraordinary; but it has no claws at all; as we all know well."

"Isn't it its tusks that have got it into favor?"— Thus the Ox broke in upon their conversation.— "Haven't they, perhaps, been mistaken for horns?"

"Is it possible," said the Ass, shaking its ears, "that you don't know how it has succeeded in making itself liked, and in becoming distinguished? Why, I have guessed the reason. If it hadn't been for its long ears, it never would have got into favor."

WE APPROVE OF OTHERS FOR THE VIRTUES WE SEE IN OURSELVES.

The Two Elephants

It is related, that a certain king was possessed of a tame and trained elephant, which he valued highly. The king's huntsmen having caught a wild elephant, which the trainers could neither train, break in, nor tame by any means, they devised associating him with the tame elephant, in order to accustom him to do the same things. This was accordingly tried, but without success—for the new elephant became only more shy and intractable, and in order to reduce him to submission, the trainer had recourse to chastisements, kept him in confinement and deprived him of food. While he was undergoing this hardship, the tame elephant one day said to him, "You are offending against your own interest and acting very unwisely for yourself, and that from ignorance; for if you knew all the good that they wish to do you, you would assuredly not behave in this manner."

The wild elephant then asked the tame one what it really was that they wanted to do with him and the latter replied: "To feed you better; to give you sweet waters to drink, to see to your cleanliness, and to that of the place where you lie, to give you servants to wait upon you, guard you, take care of you, and lead you forth at appointed hours known to all, so that the people will assemble in crowds to see you. Moreover, you will be covered with draperies and proceded by kettledrums and musical instruments which move the affections and excite the imagination, and you will be publicly honored and reverenced, so that no animal shall venture to cross your path, nor even any breath of air to blow in your disparagement."

"Faith! I have a mind to try it," replied the other elephant, and laying aside his wildness and stubbornness, he lent himself to everything that was required of him and thereupon was caressed, served and held in honor, and everything supplied to him in great abundance. Then, when the day of the festival had come, every attention was paid to him; he was rubbed down with the utmost care, covered with housings and a richly adorned howdah was placed upon his back, in which mounted a number of warriors armed with corselets, helmets, and clubs of iron. A guide armed with a goad seated himself astride upon his neck, a covering of mail was drawn over his trunk, at the end of which a sword was fastened by the hilt; the grooms, likewise, armed with cuirasses and iron clubs, posting themselves on either side of them, laid hold of his tusks. Then the kettledrums and castanets sounded and the procession put itself in motion, with the elephant, and proceeded to the appointed place.

When he had returned to his stable, however, the elephant thus addressed his companion: "I have made trial," said he, "of all the advantages of which you spoke to me, but I found certain additions to them concerning which I desire some explanation." "Ask what you will," said the tame elephant; and the other continued. "Tell me what were the heavy burdens that were placed upon my back?" "The howdah, with the warriors and the implements of war!" "And what was it they put around my trunk and at the end of it, and what was the object of those who held on to my tusks, and of the man who rode upon my neck?"

"Why, they covered your trunk with a coat of mail in order to preserve it from wounds, being a vital part; and they fastened to the end of it a sword, with which you might fight against the enemy. As for those who held your tusks, their business was to ward off the foe if they should attack you and to aid you in assault. Lastly, the man who rode upon your neck was to guide you wherever it was necessary that you should go." "It is for this, then," replied the wild elephant, "that they feed me so well, supply me with pure water, keep me and the litter upon which I lie so delicately clean, utter my name with applause and cover me with housings! I now perceive plainly that in all this the advantage is not equal to the annoyance, nor the benefit to the injury; and from hence forward I will assuredly be the most eager of those who have ever desired their liberty."

QUESTIONS FOR DISCUSSION

1. Have you read anything else in this unit that is similar to the fable of the two elephants? What are the similarities? What are the differences?
2. Do the subject and the form of a fable change much from one society to another?
3. Fables seem to be universal in their origin and appeal. Why do you think this is so? What does this suggest to you about human nature?

Understanding Words

Synonyms

A *synonym* is a word meaning the same thing, or almost the same thing, as another word. The following words are taken from the story you have just read. Choose the synonym for each word from the accompanying list.

1. intractable	a) degradation
2. submission	b) unmanageable
3. chastisements	c) breastplates
4. preceded	d) punishments
5. disparagement	e) led
6. cuirasses	f) subjection

If you were not sure of the meanings of some of the words, what helped you to find the synonym? If necessary, check the meanings in your dictionary.

Noun Suffixes –ment *and* –ion

Probably the endings of the words helped you in the above exercise. The common noun suffixes *–ment* and *–ion* are usually added to verbs. Make nouns out of the following verbs by adding either *–ment* or *–ion*.

conceal	bewilder	govern
express	advertise	distort

Can you think of other nouns made from verbs in this way?

Adjective Suffix –able

A verb can sometimes be made into an adjective by adding the suffix *–able*. Write the adjectives that can be made from the following verbs in this way.

love	work	like
cure	value	use

Can you think of others? What does the suffix mean?

Sometimes the suffix *–ible*, which means the same thing, is used: *visible, forcible, invincible, collapsible.* Can you think of other examples?

Many modern writers use some or all of the characteristics of the beast fable in their works. Here, for instance, is a fable by James Thurber, a twentieth-century American author. Later on you will discover the characteristics of the beast fable in other writings. Watch for them.

The Owl Who Was God

James Thurber

Once upon a starless midnight there was an owl who sat on the branch of an oak tree. Two ground moles tried to slip quietly by, unnoticed. "You!" said the owl. "Who?" they quavered, in fear and astonishment, for they could not believe it was possible for anyone to see them in that thick darkness. "You two!" said the owl. The moles hurried away and told the other creatures of the field and forest that the owl was the greatest and wisest of all animals because he could answer any question. "I'll see about that," said a secretary bird, and he called on the owl one night when it was again very dark. "How many claws am I holding up?" said the secretary bird. "Two," said the owl, and that was right. "Can you give me another expression for 'that is to say' or 'namely'?" asked the secretary bird. "To wit," said the owl. "Why does a lover call on his love?" asked the secretary bird. "To woo," said the owl.

The secretary bird hastened back to the other creatures and reported that the owl was indeed the greatest and wisest animal in the world because he could see in the dark and because he could answer any question. "Can he see in the daytime, too?" asked a red fox. "Yes," echoed a dormouse and a French poodle. "Can he see in the daytime, too?" All the other creatures laughed loudly at this silly question, and they set upon the red fox and his friends and drove them out of the region. Then they sent a messenger to the owl and asked him to be their leader.

When the owl appeared among the animals it was high noon and the sun was shining brightly. He walked very slowly, which gave him an appearance of great dignity, and he peered about him with large, staring eyes, which gave him an air of tremendous importance. "He's God!" screamed a Plymouth Rock hen. And the others took up the cry "He's God!" So they followed him wherever he went and when he began to bump into things they began to bump into things, too. Finally he came to a concrete highway and he started up the middle of it and all the other creatures followed him. Presently a hawk, who was acting as outrider, observed a truck coming towards them at fifty miles an hour, and he reported to the secretary bird and the secretary bird reported to the owl. "There's danger ahead," said the secretary bird. "To wit?" said the owl. The secretary bird told him. "Aren't you afraid?" he asked. "Who?" said the owl calmly, for he could not see the truck. "He's God!" cried all the creatures again, and they were still crying "He's God!" when the truck hit them and ran them down. Some of the animals were merely injured, but most of them, including the owl, were killed.

YOU CAN FOOL TOO MANY OF THE PEOPLE TOO MUCH OF THE TIME

QUESTION FOR DISCUSSION

The moral to this fable is a parody of a famous quotation. Do you know what it is? Does an understanding of the source increase your enjoyment of the fable? Why?

Parables

Let us turn now to another storied form, the *parable*. Most of the parables you know come from the Bible. Parables also are a source of many allusions. Such phrases as "a stray lamb," "a good Samaritan," and "killing the fatted calf" are all allusions to biblical parables. It is fun to study parables and fables together because while they have many things in common, they also have many interesting differences. Here are two parables which you probably already know. Both are from the King James Version of the Bible. You may find the language a little old-fashioned and difficult to read, but most people still think this is the most beautifully written version of the Bible.

The Parable of the Sower

St. Matthew 13:1–9

Antonio Frasconi, 1954

1 The same day went Jesus out of the house, and sat by the sea side.

2 And great multitudes were gathered together unto him, so that he went into a ship, and sat; and the whole multitude stood on the shore.

3 And he spake many things unto them in parables, saying, Behold, a sower went forth to sow;

4 And when he sowed, some seeds fell by the way side, and the fowls came and devoured them up:

5 Some fell upon stony places, where they had not much earth: and forthwith they sprung up, because they had no deepness of earth:

6 And when the sun was up, they were scorched; and because they had no root, they withered away.

7 And some fell among thorns; and the thorns sprung up, and choked them:

8 But other fell into good ground, and brought forth fruit, some an hundredfold, some sixtyfold, some thirtyfold.

9 Who hath ears to hear, let him hear.

The Parable of the Sower

The Parable of the Prodigal Son

St. Luke 15:11–32

11 And he said, A certain man had two sons:

12 And the younger of them said to his father, Father, give me the portion of goods that falleth to me. And he divided unto them his living.

13 And not many days after the younger son gathered all together, and took his journey into a far country, and there wasted his substance with riotous living.

14 And when he had spent all, there arose a mighty famine in that land; and he began to be in want.

15 And he went and joined himself to a citizen of that country; and he sent him into his fields to feed swine.

16 And he would fain have filled his belly with the husks that the swine did eat: and no man gave unto him.

17 And when he came to himself, he said, How many hired servants of my father's have bread enough and to spare, and I perish with hunger!

18 I will arise and go to my father, and will say unto him, Father, I have sinned against heaven, and before thee,

19 And am no more worthy to be called thy son: make me as one of thy hired servants.

20 And he arose, and came to his father. But when he was yet a great way off, his father saw him, and had compassion, and ran, and fell on his neck, and kissed him.

21 And the son said unto him, Father, I have sinned against heaven, and in thy sight, and am no more worthy to be called thy son.

22 But the father said to his servants. Bring forth the best robe, and put it on him; and put a ring on his hand, and shoes on his feet;

23 And bring hither the fatted calf, and kill it; and let us eat, and be merry:

24 For this my son was dead, and is alive again; he was lost and is found. And they began to be merry.

25 Now his elder son was in the field: and as he came and drew nigh to the house, he heard music and dancing.

The Return of the Prodigal Son,
by Rembrandt

26 And he called one of the servants, and asked what these things meant.

27 And he said unto him, Thy brother is come; and thy father hath killed the fatted calf, because he hath received him safe and sound.

28 And he was angry, and would not go in: therefore came his father out, and entreated him.

29 And he answering said to his father, Lo, these many years do I serve thee, neither transgressed I at any time thy commandment; and yet thou never gavest me a kid, that I might make merry with my friends:

30 But as soon as this thy son was come, which hath devoured thy living with harlots, thou hast killed for him the fatted calf.

31 And he said unto him, Son, thou art ever with me, and all that I have is thine.

32 It was meet that we should make merry, and be glad: for this thy brother was dead, and is alive again; and was lost, and is found.

A SUMMING UP

1. In the fables you were able to find the concrete and the abstract subjects quite easily. What are the concrete subjects of these two parables? What are the abstract subjects?
2. Can you see any differences between the abstract subjects of fables and those of parables?
3. The form of the beast fable is in two parts—story and moral. What is the form of the parable?
4. You have discussed one of the differences in form between the fable and the parable. But there is another, more obvious difference, which is, in a way, more important. What do you think it is?

The Parable of
the Prodigal Son

15

5. Can you see any relationship between the form and subject of the fable and the form and subject of the parable?
6. In class discussion, try to work out a definition of the parable which covers all the major characteristics of the form.
7. Can you think of why parables, like fables, seem to come from all peoples in history? Does this suggest anything to you?

SUGGESTIONS FOR COMPOSITION

1. The fable about the lion and the mouse probably began in Africa. Suppose instead that it had begun with the American Indians. What would the story have been like? What animals would have been featured? What type of trap or snare would have been used? Rewrite the fable in a completely different setting—an American Indian setting, an Eskimo setting, or a setting of your own choice.
2. Compile in class a list of human failings or weaknesses or characteristics. From this list, select one item and write a beast fable to illustrate it. Be sure to add a well-phrased moral tag.
3. In a short composition, discuss the differences and similarities between fables and parables.

Proverbs

The moral of a fable or a parable can frequently take the form of a *proverb*. Discuss with your teacher the definition of a proverb. In what way is it different from a fable or parable? Below is a list of proverbs, some of which you may already know. See how many you can add to the list. Then take one or two and write a fable or a parable to go before it.

A stitch in time saves nine.
All that glitters is not gold.
A fool and his money are soon parted.
Pride goeth before destruction, and a haughty spirit before a fall.
Many hands make light labor.

Go to the ant, thou sluggard; consider her ways and be wise: which
provideth her meat in the summer, and gathereth food in the
harvest.

There's many a slip 'twixt cup and lip.

A bird in the hand is worth two in the bush.

A friend in need is a friend indeed.

Don't count your chickens before they are hatched.

It is an ill wind that blows nobody good.

Don't sell a pig to buy bacon.

As a whirlwind passes, so is the wicked man no more; but the righteous
is an everlasting foundation.

The fear of the Lord is the beginning of knowledge, but fools despise
wisdom and instruction.

THERE'S MANY A SLIP....

SUGGESTIONS FOR COMPOSITION

1. Find or make up a proverb to illustrate the abstract subject of "The Two
Elephants." Try to make it as brief and well-balanced as you can.
Compare yours with those of the rest of the class, and decide which is
the best.
2. Write an account of an incident you know or have heard of which
illustrates one of the fables or proverbs you have read.

SUGGESTIONS FOR READING

Aesop's Fables, ill. by Fritz Kredel. Grosset & Dunlap, 1947.
The Aesop for Children, ill. by Milo Winter. Rand McNally, 1955.
Thurber, James, *Fables for Our Times; Further Fables for Our Times*. (Amusing
parodies on ancient fables.) Harper & Row, 1940.

Mythology

How was the world made? Where did the first people live? Why are we here?

People have sought answers to all of these questions for thousands of years. One way man answers these questions is through myths—stories that tell how the world was made, how the seasons came about, who rules the world, and what man's future may be.

In this unit you will be reading some of the best-known myths. As you read, try to see how the stories we call *myths* differ from the stories we call *fables* or *proverbs*. You will read about the wily Loki and meet brave Prometheus, who stole fire from the gods. You will read myths which come from many hundreds of miles apart. Yet you will notice something surprising. As they explain the creation of the world or describe a hero, for instance, many of the myths may resemble each other.

Why is this so? We are not sure. Perhaps the reason is that all people came from the same part of the world and carried their myths with them. Or perhaps it is because all people at times have been interested in seeking answers to the same questions we puzzle over today: Why was I born? Where did the spring come from? Who made the world? These questions were answered in the form of stories, stories made up by unknown peoples. Of course, at one time these myths were widely believed as representing fact.

Greek Myths

GREEK GODS

Before we read the stories the Greeks told to explain their way of life, let us look briefly at the world they lived in—and the even more exciting world they imagined.

The Greeks lived on a group of tiny islands and jagged peninsulas in the Mediterranean Sea. Although their world may seem very small to us, to them it was a dramatic panorama. There were mountains towering high into the sky, lush plains, and an ever-threatening though beautiful blue sea. Because of that sea, only the bravest sailors ventured very far from their homes. Nevertheless they imagined a wonderful world within and beyond their horizon.

The Greeks believed that the world was flat and round like a plate and that they lived right in the center of it. In the middle of Greece itself was Mount Olympus, the home of the gods. Around the earth steadily flowed the River Ocean; untroubled by storms, it supplied the water for the sea and the rivers.

To the north lived the Hyperboreans, a happy race. They dwelt beyond the cold mountains and chilling winds that blasted the people of Greece. Their world was one of perpetual spring. Their country could not be reached by land or sea. They never worked; they were never sick; and they never died.

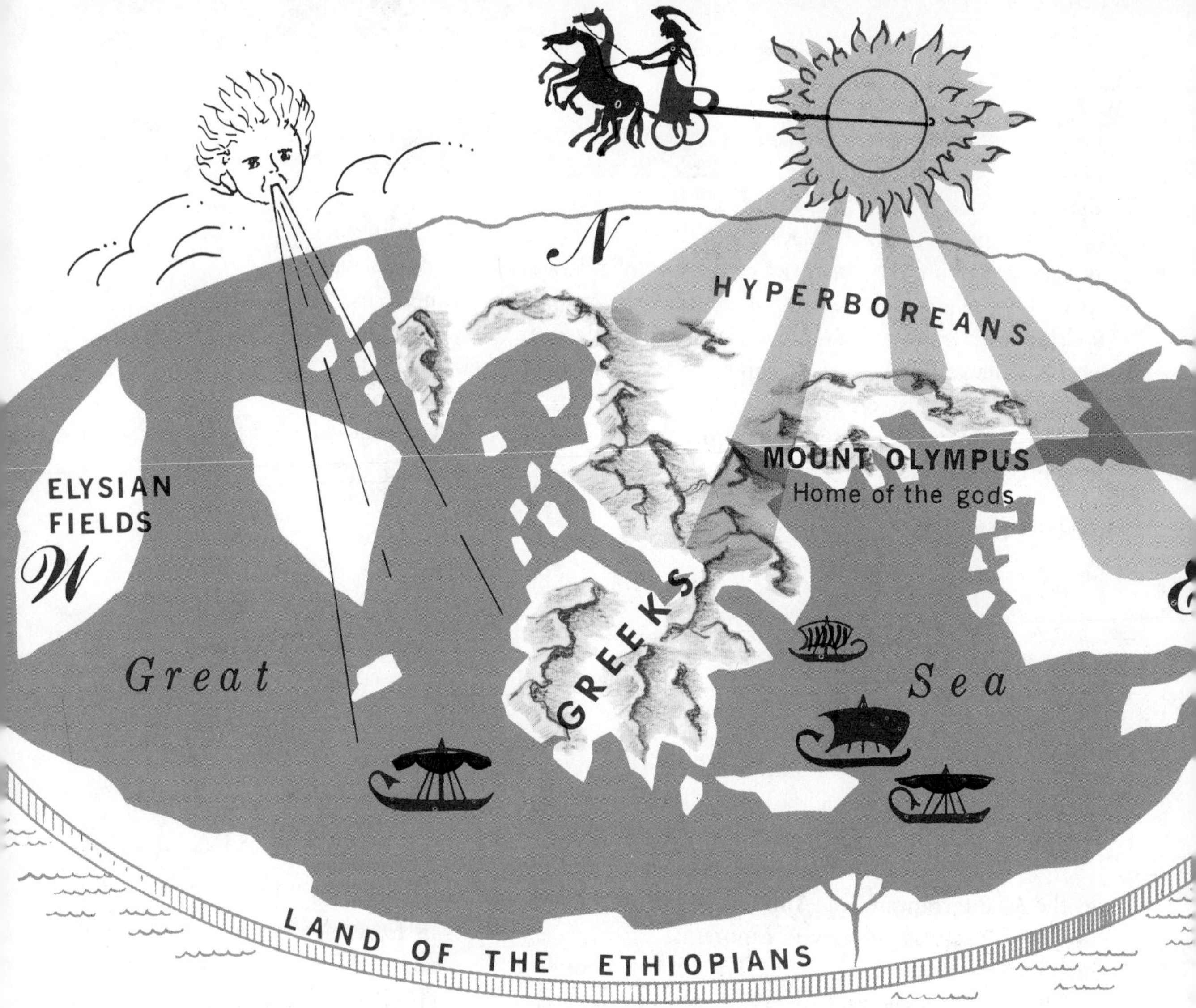
N
HYPERBOREANS
MOUNT OLYMPUS
Home of the gods
ELYSIAN FIELDS
W
GREEKS
Great
Sea
LAND OF THE ETHIOPIANS
River S Ocean

GREEK WORLD

To the south lived another happy people, the Ethiopians. To the west lay the Elysian Fields, where heroes and other mortals were taken to live in blissful immortality. From the east rose the dawn, sun, moon, and stars. It was from there that the sun-god drove his chariot on his daily journey across the sky.

Because the Greeks had not yet ventured far from home, they imagined distant lands to be peopled with giants and cruel gods. You will be reading about some of these characters in this section.

The first story you will read is an account of the beginning of the world according to the ancient Greeks. See if you can determine the pattern that develops. Does this picture of the origin of the earth in any way resemble your own ideas about that event?

The Creation

Barbara Drake

In the beginning, there was neither light nor dark, places nor things, up nor down. There was nothing. This nothingness was called Chaos; in short, it was simply the lack of either things or order. Even in Chaos, however, lay the possibilities of order, and these possibilities were like seeds from which, in time, all things grew.

The first thing to grow out of Chaos was Night, spreading its wings of darkness like a giant bird. Next to emerge was Erebus, the bottomless place where Death lives. Then Night laid a silver egg, out of which hatched Eros, or Love. The beginning of Love was also the beginning of light, life, and joy.

Mother Earth, or Gaia, and Father Heaven, called Uranus, then came into this universe of light and dark, and life and death. Rain fell from Heaven and lakes, oceans, and rivers were made, and green plants began to spring out of the Earth.

Uranus and Gaia had quite a large number of children. Their first three offspring were ugly monsters; each had fifty heads and a hundred hands. Uranus was so disappointed with them that he immediately shut them up inside the earth. The Cyclopes were the next three children of Gaia and Uranus. Each Cyclops had one enormous, glassy eye in the middle of his forehead. Although they were cleverer than the three monsters and were even skilled at making weapons from metal, Uranus shut them away, too. He thought they were ugly and perhaps even dangerous.

The Titans, six sons and six daughters, were the last of Uranus and Gaia's children. Compared with their ferocious older brothers, they were rather good-looking and well-behaved.

Because Gaia was upset about the fate of the monsters and the Cyclopes, and feared the same treatment for the Titans, she called them together. Gaia warned them that the same thing might happen to them if they didn't do something about Uranus first.

But, big and strong as they were, the Titans were afraid of their father. Each one said he couldn't possibly think of anything to do, and each suggested that one of the other Titans find a solution. Finally, Cronus, the youngest Titan, came up with a secret plan. Although it was not a very clever plan, it took his father by surprise. Uranus was so used to running things his own way that he simply did not expect any opposition.

This is what happened: Cronus got a sharp sickle from his mother and attacked Uranus with it, badly wounding him. Uranus was in too much pain to fight back, so all he could do was flee. But as he fled upwards, as high as he could go, he shouted down to Cronus, "You'll get the same treatment from one of your children someday. Beware!"

And since the exile of Uranus, the sky has never come near the earth. Some of the blood of Uranus fell to the earth, though, and turned into the Giants and the Erinyes, or Furies. These terrible creatures had live snakes for hair, and they chased wrong-doers about until they were punished.

If Gaia expected sympathy and co-operation from Cronus, she was greatly disappointed. Instead of freeing his older brothers, Cronus quickly took his father's place as ruler of the world and made his Titan brothers his generals. To Oceanus, he gave the rule of the River-Ocean that circled the world. He gave control of all light in the world to his brother Hyperion. The children of Hyperion, the Sun, the Moon, and the Dawn, rode across the sky in their chariots once each day.

Although Gaia was angry at her high-handed son Cronus, she had no say in the matter for the time being. And the Titans became known as the Elder Gods.

QUESTIONS FOR DISCUSSION

1. What is this myth about? Is it about a family quarrel? Or about the beginning of the world? Is it about both? Explain.
2. What was Uranus's attitude toward his first six children? What was Gaia's reaction? In what way do these reactions influence later events?
3. Note how certain elements in this myth are sharply contrasted. Out of Chaos comes order, out of darkness, light. What other contrasts can you discover? Do they help to reveal the subject? In what way?
4. This myth falls into a typical beginning, middle, and end narrative pattern. Draw a simple diagram and fill in the incidents.

beginning	middle	end

5. Look back over the incidents you selected for your diagram. Is there a general movement from disorder to order? Explain. In what way does this reflect the subject?
6. Do you notice anything in this episode that hints at (or *foreshadows*) the coming downfall of Cronus? Why do you think authors often hint in advance of dire events yet to come?
7. Does this myth seem to be told from an impersonal viewpoint, or does the teller seem to scold the gods for certain actions?
8. *Poetic justice* is a term used to describe the reward of virtue and punishment of vice that occurs in many works of literature. Do you detect anything akin to poetic justice at work in this myth? Explain.
9. The new order described in this myth was not perfect. As Uranus fled, his drops of blood turned into Furies. What do you suppose they are an attempt to explain?

Understanding Words

Context Clues

Sometimes a writer will use a comparison that helps to define a word he uses. Of Gaia's last children we are told that "Compared with their *ferocious* older brothers, they were rather good-looking and well-behaved." What do you think *ferocious* means?

SUGGESTION FOR COMPOSITION

Trace the steps in this myth from chaos to the separation of earth, sky, and sea. Is it very much like what science tells us about the history of the earth? Write a paragraph pointing out some of the more obvious similarities.

Man has always liked to look back to "the good old days," to a time when things were supposedly much better than they are in his present age. The Greeks called this perfect time of man the Golden Age.

The Golden Age

Barbara Drake

The Golden Age was a time of perfect peace and happiness. Every day was like spring; flowers bloomed the year round. The men of the Golden Age, the subjects of Cronus, were greatly loved by the gods. They lived very much like gods, without cares or labor. The earth provided them with all the food they needed — acorns, wild fruit, and honey that dripped from the trees. They were rich in flocks and drank the milk of sheep and goats. They knew no pain, no worry, and no wars. They never quarreled. Indeed, they were always happy, and their time was spent in dancing and singing. There were no mortal descendants of this golden race, for there were no women, but they were such a good race that, at their passing, their pure spirits remained on earth as the guardians of mankind.

QUESTIONS FOR DISCUSSION

1. Consider the Greek idea of the Golden Age. Does it remind you of any other such age you have read about? What does it tell us about the Greeks?
2. Is the subject of "The Golden Age" about ideas as well as things? Can you state both subjects?

SUGGESTED ACTIVITIES

1. If you were Cronus, setting up your own paradise, what would it be like? Who would live there? What would people do all day long? What would they eat? Write a paragraph describing your golden age, or make a brief speech to the class about this subject.
2. The Greek gods were not always models of virtue and honor. Some of the Greek heroes put the gods to shame in matters of conduct. Consider-

ing all this, do you think the people behaved better than they would have if they had not been conscious of the nearness of the gods? Why do you think the Greeks also created gods who often acted in ways that men could not understand?

Do you remember what Uranus shouted back as he fled from his victorious son? Cronus remembered all too well. What he did about it might have seemed sensible to him, but it may be a bit upsetting to the rest of us. As you read, compare the pattern that develops here with the pattern you found in "The Creation." Are the patterns similar, or not?

The War in Heaven

Barbara Drake

Cronus never forgot his father's warning that he, too, would be overthrown by one of his own children someday. To prevent this, he swallowed his first five children as soon as they were born. Hestia, Demeter, and Hera, his daughters, and his sons, Hades and Poseidon, had all been swallowed by the time the sixth child was on its way.

His wife, Rhea, was very upset by this. She went to her mother, Gaia, and asked how she could put a stop to this unfatherly behavior. Gaia, having had a similar problem with her husband Uranus, was more than happy to advise her. She told Rhea to go to the island of Crete and to hide her newborn child in a secret cave on Mount Ida, a mountain there. She was to give Cronus a stone, wrapped in blankets, instead of the baby. Gaia said that Cronus would never know the difference.

Rhea did as Gaia had told her, and Cronus swallowed the bundle —stone, blankets, and all. He never even looked up from what he was doing.

The child was a son, Zeus, who grew up on Crete, well cared for by nymphs and shepherds. He could not travel to the palace, however, without endangering his life. Finally, one day Rhea sent the messenger Metis to visit Zeus and to show him how to brew a strong poison from herbs. The messenger told Zeus to go to Cronus's palace and hide there until he could get a chance to put the poison into Cronus's wine cup. Zeus did this, and one night, while he was hiding under the supper table, he got his chance. Cronus had eaten a big meal and was sitting, drowsing, over his wine. Zeus slipped the poison into the cup.

As soon as Cronus had drunk the poisoned wine, an amazing thing happened. He got so sick that up came his first five children as well as the big stone wrapped in blankets.

Cronus had a strong stomach, though, and the poison only made him sick for a while. Although Zeus and his brothers, Hades and Poseidon, quickly tied their father to his chair, he was soon shouting for his brother Titans. And thus began a battle that lasted for years. The Elder Gods were led by the Titan Atlas, and the younger gods were led by Zeus. First the Titans chased the younger gods up Mount Olympus, and it looked as if the Elder Gods were winning. But Zeus went to see his grandmother, Gaia, since it had been her advice that had brought things to this pass anyway.

Gaia was old, and she was getting impatient and more than a little irritated with the quarrels of her family. Besides, she was still upset that her husband Uranus had shut their first six children in the earth. So she said to Zeus, "You have freed your mother's firstborn children, but until you free mine, you will not be victorious."

Zeus did not understand Gaia's words, for he knew little of his family history. So he shrugged his shoulders and went back to the battle.

The battle between the Titans and the younger gods might have raged even longer had it not been for Prometheus, a son of Iapetus, one of the Titans. For Prometheus could see into the future, and he knew that the reign of Cronus and the Titans was ending. He thought it would be best to settle things with the least possible damage to everyone concerned, so he asked the other Titans to make a truce. They shouted him down. "Not a chance!" they said.

Prometheus then went to Zeus and told him all about the monstrous children of Gaia and Uranus. He said to Zeus, "If you release them, they will fight on your side." Zeus went to the underworld and freed the hundred-handed monsters and the Cyclopes. The monsters fought against the Titans with all their strength, and the Cyclopes made armor and weapons for Zeus and his brothers. They made a helmet for Hades which made him invisible, a three-pronged spear for Poseidon, and thunderbolts for Zeus.

The younger gods now quickly won the war. Some of the Titans were flung into the underworld, some escaped and disappeared forever, and Atlas was made to stand at the western edge of the world, holding up the heavens. Only Prometheus and one or two of the Titan women were saved. Perhaps Prometheus was saved because of the help he had given to Zeus and the younger gods.

QUESTIONS FOR DISCUSSION

1. Note how, as the fortunes of Zeus rise, those of Cronus decline. Try showing this on a simple line graph. It might look like this:

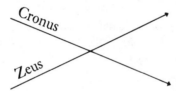

   What events mark the rise of one and the fall of the other?
2. Everything in this myth rises to one event, then moves down again. What event is the "turning point"?

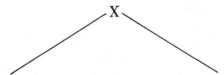

3. In the creation myth you saw how the action moved from disorder to order. Here, there is a reversal. Show how the narrative patterns of the two myths contrast sharply. In what way does this reflect the subject? What other comparisons and contrasts can you find?
4. We have spoken of poetic justice before. Do you detect any poetic justice in Cronus's fate? Explain.
5. If we continue to read these stories as explanations of natural phenomena, what might the war in heaven represent? Have you heard of a similar story from another source?

6. What have you noticed about the way these stories have been told? A great deal of violence and bloodshed has been recorded. Has the writer passed any judgment? Has he given any opinions? Does this kind of writing remind you of other literature you have studied? What does this similarity tell you about the origins of these stories?

7. There seems to be an inevitability about everything that happens, and no amount of scheming on the part of the gods can prevent things from happening once the course has been set. For instance, Zeus had to win the war, but what previous action made this necessary? Can you see a pattern, one event making another inevitable, or is it just luck? Discuss.

Understanding Words

A Familiar Word

"... her advice that had brought things to this *pass*...." What does the word mean as it is used here? Is it a noun or a verb? What other meanings can you think of for the word *pass*, when it is used as a noun?

Now that the dust of battle has settled, Zeus puts his house in order. Note carefully the names of his family; you will be hearing about them for the rest of your life.

The Reign of Zeus

Barbara Drake

After the war was over, Zeus said that he would be the head of gods and men because he had done the most to overthrow the Titans and lead the younger gods to victory. But he divided the rule of the kingdom with Poseidon and Hades. Zeus ruled the heavens, Poseidon controlled the ocean, and Hades took charge of the world of the dead, or underworld. All the gods and goddesses and their children settled themselves on Mount Olympus, their new home.

Zeus kept an eye on everything, everywhere. Poseidon looked after the sea and enjoyed riding over the waves in his golden chariot. When he was in a bad mood, which was often enough, he stirred up storms with his trident, a three-pronged spear, wrecking ships and drowning sailors. When he was bored, he would go to Mount Olympus and sit around playing games and gossiping with the other gods. After Hades became god of the underworld, he rarely left home, and became a very gloomy fellow. He spent most of his time making lists of his wealth and sorting the dead into their proper groups.

There were twelve important Olympian gods and goddesses, and they were all so different that they rarely all agreed on anything. Fortunately, each one had his or her own special duties, and each was an expert on something, so they managed to get along and even depended on each other for some things.

Zeus married his sister Hera, who then became the queen of the gods. She was also the goddess of marriage, but she spent much of her time nagging Zeus or spying on him, for she was vain and jealous. It is no wonder that Zeus spent a great deal of time away from home, changing himself into a bull, an eagle, a cloud, or whatever fancy struck him, so that Hera could not find him.

Athena, goddess of war and wisdom, was the offspring of Zeus. She sprang forth from his head completely armed. And she was his favorite child.

Zeus tossed Hephaestus out of Olympus because of a quarrel, and he fell for nine days and nights before he finally landed on the Greek island of Lemnos. The fall made him lame in one foot, but he hobbled about on Lemnos, doing the best he could. He was very good at forging things out of metal, and when Zeus saw what a skilled artisan he was, he brought him back to Olympus where he could be useful, although he was both lame and homely.

Aphrodite, the goddess of love, came out of the foam of the sea. She just appeared in a seashell one day, floating off the coast of Cythera. The most beautiful of the goddesses, Aphrodite had an embroidered girdle, or sash, which could cause anyone to fall in love with her when she wore it. But Zeus, grateful to Hephaestus for a service he had done, married Aphrodite to this most homely of the gods.

Aphrodite, however, spent a lot of time flirting with Ares. Ares, the son of Zeus and Hera, was the god of war. He was often drunk, always quarrelsome, and not very well thought of by the other gods and goddesses. But Aphrodite found him more interesting than her plain, hard-working husband.

Phoebus Apollo and Artemis were the twins of Zeus and Leto, a Titan woman. They were both skilled in archery and carried bows and arrows — golden for Apollo, and silver for Artemis. They were also good at healing almost any illness. In many ways, though, they were the opposites of one another. Artemis was goddess of the moon and of hunting, and she was also the guardian of children and young animals. She had no desire to get married, for she preferred hunting and running through the woods to household matters. The most handsome of the gods, Apollo was the sun god and god of light. He disliked any sort of darkness or trickery, so he was also the god of truth, prophecy, and music.

Hermes was the son of Zeus and Atlas's daughter, Maia. When he was only a few hours old he stole some cattle from Apollo and used pieces of their hide stretched across a tortoise shell to make a kind of harp. He called his musical instrument a lyre. Apollo was enraged at the theft of his cattle, but Hermes shrewdly offered to give Apollo the lyre in exchange for the cattle he had stolen. Since the lyre was just what Apollo needed for his music and prophecy-making, he promised to forgive Hermes, on condition that Zeus would find him something more useful to do than steal property. Zeus immediately saw where Hermes' talent lay, and made him god of merchants and trade. He gave Hermes winged sandals and a winged cap, with which he could travel more quickly than anyone else, and Hermes became the messenger of the gods. He was seen at all the important battles, delivering messages, and he raced back and forth when there were arguments. He seemed to be every place at once.

Hestia, Zeus's sister, was the goddess of home and family. She never quarreled, but set a good example for the others by being quiet, modest, and kind. This most peaceful of the twelve Olympian gods and goddesses spent most of her time at home. Fires in her honor were kept burning on all the hearths in the world.

In addition to the twelve gods and goddesses of heaven, there were three important earth gods — Demeter, Dionysus, and Pan. Demeter, Zeus's sister, was goddess of the harvest, Dionysus was the god of wine, and Pan was god of the shepherds. All three were important in the daily affairs of man.

At one time Demeter looked after the earth and kept it fruitful all year long. She later changed her policy. Hades decided one day that he needed a wife to sit by him and help him with all the business in the underworld. Since he did not want to waste any time in selecting a wife, he rode up to the surface of earth one day, and saw Persephone, Demeter's daughter. She was very beautiful, so he snatched her up and carried her home to the underworld with him. Demeter was so unhappy at the loss of

Birth of Athena,
Greek Amphora (detail),
6th century B.C.,
Museum of Fine Arts, Boston

her daughter that she refused to tend her garden. All the flowers and other plants died, and the leaves fell off the trees. Persephone was unhappy in the underworld, too, and she refused to eat anything in Hades's kingdom, except for six pomegranate seeds. Hades saw how miserable she was and finally allowed her to visit her mother on earth for six months of each year, but because of the six seeds she had eaten, she had to return to live with him in the underworld for the other six months. This was the beginning of the seasons, for Demeter would make the plants grow only during the time that Persephone lived with her.

Zeus was Dionysus's father, but his mother was a mortal woman, Semele. Perhaps because he was the only important god to be half mortal, Dionysus died each year. After the grapes had been harvested and the wine made, Dionysus was torn to pieces by his own drunken followers. But each spring he was reborn. Dionysus sometimes looked like a carefree, laughing youth, but at other times he appeared to be an evil old drunkard. He was able to look like both, for he was not only the god of joy, but also the god of madness.

Pan was a solitary god. Sometimes he was not seen by the shepherds whom he protected, and they could only hear the music of his reed pipe. He had invented the pipe himself and it could sound both sad and gay, lonely and sweet. Pan often admired the girls he saw as he wandered through the woods and fields. But he was half man and half goat, and the girls ran from Pan because he was so ugly.

The Reign of Zeus

Have you ever been invited to a large party while you were visiting in a strange city? Could you remember who everybody was, and get their relationships straight? Perhaps you feel equally bewildered after this introduction to the gods on Mount Olympus. The following questions are asked simply to help you get to know the gods better and feel at home with them.

1. Zeus, of course, was the most powerful god on Mount Olympus. Who shared the power with him to rule the sea and the underworld?
2. Who was the queen of the gods? What was she like?
3. What was strange about the birth of Athena? What was she like?
4. Who was Hephaestus?
5. Old King Solomon was said to have had a thousand wives. We don't know how many Zeus had, but Hera, the queen, was obviously not his only wife. Who were the twin children of Zeus and Leto?
6. Who was Hermes, and what was his job?
7. Who was the goddess of love and beauty? Who was her husband?
8. Who was the god of war?
9. Who was the most peace-loving of the gods and goddesses? What was her relationship to Zeus?
10. Zeus had yet another sister, besides Hera and Hestia. Who was she? Who was her daughter?
11. Which god had a mortal mother?
12. Can you describe Pan?

SUGGESTED ACTIVITIES

1. Make a "family tree" of the gods to help you keep them straight. You could make a small one for your notebook, or a large one for the bulletin board. Find out more about one of the gods or goddesses, and report your findings to the class. If several people each prepare a report, the class will learn quite a lot about several of the gods.
2. Now that you have met the Greek gods on their home ground and feel somewhat familiar with them, try to decide what they represent as a group. Do they seem to represent or symbolize good? Evil? Things which happen to man over which he has no control? Justify your answer. Show how the actions of the gods seem to indicate one or more of these things.

This selection is the first in a chain of stories about Prometheus and mankind. Here you will learn how Prometheus carried out a very special assignment given to him and his brother Epimetheus by the gods.

Prometheus Creates Man

Barbara Drake

The quarrelsome men of the Silver Age had all been drowned in a great flood. But now that the war between the Titans and the Olympians was over, the time was right for a new race of men to be created. Since the twelve Olympian gods and goddesses were busy ruling, playing, and quarreling among themselves, the gods assigned this task to Prometheus and Epimetheus, the sons of the Titan, Iapetus.

Prometheus had sided with the Olympians in their battle with the Titans, perhaps because he could see into the future and knew that they would win. His name means "forethought" in Greek. Epimetheus was nothing like his brother. His name meant "afterthought," and he was always changing his mind about things.

Epimetheus was scatter-brained and impulsive. He wanted to do well at his share of the task of creating men, but, true to his name, he did not see the mistakes he was making until he had already made them. First

he made the birds, then the fish, and then the animals. He fashioned each creature as carefully as if it were the only one. To each he gave the gift of some fine quality which would set it apart from all the rest. He gave cunning to the fox, swiftness to the antelope, wings to the eagle, and a hard shell to the turtle, and so on. When he had finished with all the creatures, he turned to the task he had saved till the very end, that of making man. He first thought of giving man a warm, furry hide, but he had already given that to the bear. Then he thought of giving man fierce claws, but they had been given to the tiger. Sharp horns, a leathery skin, eyes that can see in the dark — Epimetheus tried desperately to remember some quality that he could give to man, whom he had thought to make the best of his creations, but there was nothing left to give. He realized his mistake and begged Prometheus to help him.

"Prometheus," he cried. "What can I do?"

"It's too bad you didn't think about this when you began," said Prometheus. "But if man is going to be soft, weak, naked, and slow, the least I can do is see that he is not stupid." So saying, Prometheus took a bit of clay and shaped it into a small likeness of the noble gods. He stood man upright, so that he might always look up to the heavens. Then he breathed life into the clay and gave man a superior mind with which he could reason, plan, remember, and dream. In this way Prometheus set man above all the other creatures.

QUESTIONS FOR DISCUSSION

1. Can you state the subject of this myth in two ways? Does it seem to be about ideas as well as things?
2. This myth draws a sharp contrast between the two brothers. In what way did they differ? How did this difference affect the story itself?
3. This myth has a beginning, middle, and end pattern. Try to identify each part.

Understanding Words

A Familiar Word

We are accustomed to seeing the word *fashion* used as a noun, usually in relation to dress. The latest *fashions* are the up-to-date styles in clothing. Here the word is used as a verb. What does the context tell you is the meaning of "He *fashioned* each creature ..."?

The Greeks decided that some of the gods were for man, and that others were against him. Some, it seemed, went out of their way to make life miserable for man. What do you think the Greeks were trying to explain by creating such gods?

You are about to meet Prometheus again. Does he change in character here from the Prometheus you read about in "The War in Heaven"?

Prometheus Brings Fire to Man

Barbara Drake

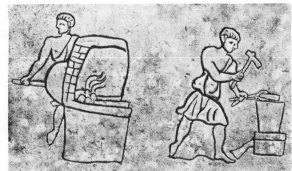

The great flood that ended the Silver Age not only destroyed the men of the time, it also shook loose all the ice and snow which had been stuck up in the northern part of the world. The climate of the earth was no longer mild, and the new men Prometheus had made suffered greatly from the cold. They spent a lot of time complaining about the bad weather and said that it was a cruel joke for someone to create them just to lead such miserable lives.

"These men are more disagreeable than the others," said Zeus.

When Prometheus heard this, he knew that Zeus would soon decide to drown these men, too, unless something was done. The best thing Prometheus could think of to make men's lives better was the gift of fire. With fire, man could warm himself, cook his food, and forge metal for tools and weapons. He could make lights at night, so that the world would not seem such a dark, dreary place. Prometheus also knew that Zeus would never agree to this, so he made his plans secretly.

He gave a last look at Olympus, for he knew he could never return, and he told Athena good-bye. She had been his best friend there. Without another backward glance, Prometheus set out for the fiery home of the sun.

He broke from the sun a fragment of glowing coal and, hiding it in the hollow of a giant fennel-stalk, he carried it down to earth. There he lit a central fire and showed men how to use it. Then he taught them how to make it for themselves by rubbing sticks together.

Sitting around their evening fires, eating roast ox or lamb, men said to each other than they didn't know how they had survived before, without this fine thing, fire.

QUESTIONS FOR DISCUSSION

1. Note the geographical changes that have taken place in the world since the time of Cronus. Compare this with the scientific information we have today. Is there any similarity? How do you think these changes affected the lives of people?
2. What attitude did Zeus have toward mankind? How did his attitude differ from that of Prometheus?
3. In this story Zeus is the "bad guy" and Prometheus the "good guy." How does the teller choose details that help you to know this? Are any other contrasts at work in this tale? Do they aid in revealing the subject and moving the story forward? In what way?
4. In this myth the author made Prometheus a symbol of something very desirable. A *symbol* is a person or an object that stands for an idea. What do you think Prometheus might symbolize? What does *promethean* mean?

The Punishment of Prometheus

Barbara Drake

When Zeus heard that Prometheus had given fire to man, he was terribly angry. He didn't really care whether men had fire or not, but the fact that Prometheus had aided man without his permission made him furious. It was the principle of the thing. Zeus decided to make an example of Prometheus.

He ordered Prometheus to be seized and chained to the face of a great cliff in the Caucasian Mountains. A giant vulture was sent to eat at Prometheus's liver all day long. Each night his liver grew back, and there was no end to his suffering.

Zeus was a great schemer. He wanted revenge on Prometheus, but he also had an idea of how to make use of him. After a while, he sent Hermes to Prometheus with an offer.

Hermes told Prometheus that Zeus saw no reason to continue the punishment if Prometheus would make a reasonable agreement. Since Prometheus could see into the future, he would be able to tell Zeus the identity of the mother of the child destined to overthrow him, just as he had overthrown his father and Cronus had overthrown Uranus before him. For that information, Zeus would free Prometheus.

Prometheus answered that he had already done more favors for Zeus than Zeus had ever done for him, and that he would not submit to blackmail. "I am in the right," said Prometheus. "And I would rather suffer than give in to an unreasonable tyrant."

This answer made Zeus wild with anger, but he could do nothing more than rave.

QUESTIONS FOR DISCUSSION

1. This story is about the punishment that Zeus, in his rage, meted out to Prometheus. But is it about anything else? Think about what Zeus, the ruler of the world, seems to symbolize, and what Prometheus stands for? What else does this myth concern?
2. What is the attitude of the teller of this myth toward Zeus? Toward Prometheus? How do you know? How did Zeus feel about Prometheus's act? What did Prometheus think of Zeus? How do you know?
3. Stories often concern conflict. Do you see conflict in this tale? Explain.

Understanding Words

Context Clues

Prometheus said "... I would rather suffer than give in to an unreasonable *tyrant.*" Read the paragraphs around this sentence again. What clues can you find to the meaning of the word *tyrant?* Is a *tyrant* (a) a blackmailer, (b) an ungrateful king, (c) a ruler who exercises absolute power oppressively or brutally, or (d) a bad-tempered king?

1. Prometheus gave man the secret of fire. Today man has unlocked the secret of the sun and possesses the power of nuclear energy. Was Zeus right? Has man now become as powerful as the gods? Imagine that Hermes has just hurried into the dining room of the gods on Mount Olympus to bring news of the explosion of the first atomic bomb. What will Zeus say? Will Prometheus still say that he is right? Let your imagination have free rein, and write an account for the reaction of the gods to the news.

2. For a highly imaginative story about Prometheus, read "Paradise of Children" in *Tanglewood Tales*, by Nathaniel Hawthorne. Tell it to the class, or work up a skit for the class.

Zeus, still simmering with anger because Prometheus had defied him, decided that man also needed to be punished. He made up his mind to try his own hand at creating; *he* would design a creature to send to earth — a creature that would cause so much trouble that man would never again have time to complain about the gods.

Have you any idea what he created?

Pandora's Box

Barbara Drake

Of course Zeus was unreasonable when angry, but he didn't care. He was powerful and didn't want anyone to doubt it. From Prometheus, Zeus turned his anger upon mankind. Men were far too comfortable, so far as he was concerned.

Zeus thought of a clever plot to punish them for their disobedience, and he chuckled at his own cleverness. He would send a creation of his own to live among Prometheus's men. Zeus ordered Hephaestus to design a beautiful creature, a woman.

"She is lovely," said all the gods and goddesses when they saw her. "Let us help." Hestia gave the woman gentleness, Hermes made her light-footed, Aphrodite made her lovable, Apollo gave her a musical nature, and so on. They named her Pandora, or "all-gifted."

"Perfect," said Zeus, still chuckling. Then he sent Pandora as a gift to Prometheus's slow-witted brother Epimetheus. Epimetheus had been warned not to accept presents from Zeus, but when he saw Pandora he forgot the warning entirely. "What a fine present!" he said, and married her on the spot. For a short time they lived happily.

In Epimetheus's house there was a box left from the time when he and Prometheus had created the first creatures. They had used all the good things, but the evils were still stored in this box. When Prometheus was taken away, his parting words to Epimetheus were, "Guard the box with your life."

Epimetheus said, "Oh, I *will.*" But he forgot all about it, leaving the box to stand, gathering dust in an unused attic.

When Epimetheus was at home, Pandora made him happy by singing sweet songs, arranging the cushions in his chair to make him comfortable, and bringing him good tidbits on golden platters. But as soon as Epimetheus left the house, Pandora was off poking into cupboards, reading old letters, and in general prying into things, instead of tending to her household work. Like all the women who came after her, Pandora had great curiosity.

One day when Epimetheus was gone, Pandora found the box. It was tied round and round with ropes and padlocked shut with a thick chain. Pandora ran and got a knife from the kitchen. One by one she cut through the ropes on the box and let them fall. Then she took Epimetheus's ring of keys from the closet. He had many keys, and she tried nearly a hundred before one turned in the lock. With a loud clatter the chain fell to the floor. Now there remained only the latch, which she could easily move.

Pandora's Box

39

For a long time Pandora just sat there, looking at the dusty box. She had a strong feeling she should leave it alone. But what might it contain? A present for her? Jewels? Or perhaps something Epimetheus was ashamed of?

She lifted the lid just a crack, thinking to take a quick peek and shut it again. Instantly all sorts of evil things rushed out and flew into the world: old age, sickness, envy, revenge, worry, pain, greed, hate, and everything else bad that you can think of. These things have been loose in the world ever since, and man has never been completely happy.

But Prometheus had foreseen the day when someone might unloose these evils, and he had put into the box one good thing—hope, which even today helps man to bear the sorrows of his life.

QUESTIONS FOR DISCUSSION

1. This myth is about a young woman endowed with an avid curiosity. But it is about something else, too. Explain.
2. Whose fault was it that Pandora opened the box? Is Epimetheus to be blamed at all? In what way?
3. Why had Prometheus put hope in the chest along with all the terrible evils? What knowledge of the future of man does this imply? Did this ruin Zeus's revenge? Explain.
4. What does this myth attempt to explain about life? About human nature?
5. Does the writer of this story blame Pandora for opening the box? Does he blame Zeus? Does he think men deserved what they got? Do you know at all what he thinks?
6. A writer uses a definite pattern for the organization of his ideas in telling a story. The simple plan used in "Pandora's Box" has three parts: The why, or *cause*, of what happens; the *details* of what happens; and the "how things were changed," or the *effect*, of what happens. Can you find these three parts of the story?

Understanding Words

A Typical English Spelling

The *ch* sound, as in *latch*, is frequently spelled *tch* in English words. Make a list of words using this grapheme. Each member of the class might look up in the dictionary the origin of one word from the list. Where do most of the words come from?

Zeus, long impatient with man, would have liked to destroy him, but he was getting worried about what the other gods and goddesses thought of him. It would never do to be thought reckless and immature! So he disguised himself and went down to earth to investigate the matter thoroughly.

He was soon back at Mount Olympus in a terrible temper. Can you guess who saved man this time?

Deucalion and the Flood

Barbara Drake

After Pandora let all the evils loose in the world, mankind became even more unpleasant than were the men of the Silver Age. They complained, lied, stole, murdered, and ceased to honor the gods. The only time they mentioned the gods, in fact, was to swear at them for some trouble.

"They ought to be glad just to be alive," said Zeus. "Don't they know I could destroy them in a minute, if I wanted to?" He seriously considered doing so.

But Zeus wanted to be thought a wise and just ruler, and some of the other gods and goddesses were beginning to say that he behaved rashly more often than wisely. He decided to investigate matters on earth himself, before doing anything drastic.

Disguised as a tired, old traveler, Zeus went down to earth and visited the homes of men. In the first village he came to, men chased him away with sticks and stones. He walked on until he came to a large, rich-looking home. There the woman of the house let him stay, but she gave him moldy bread to eat and made him sleep with the cows. Everywhere he went it was the same. As he pretended to sleep, men tried to steal his shoes. Children stuck out their tongues at him and dogs snapped at his heels.

Angrier than ever, Zeus returned to Olympus and snatched up a thunderbolt, intending to do away with men forever. But Athena cried out, reminding him that it had been prophesied that one day all of creation would go up in flames. "All right," said Zeus. "Water will do just as well." He asked Poseidon to flood the land, and he sent down torrents of rain. Soon nothing remained above water except Mount Parnassus in northern Greece.

There were two good and honorable people on earth — Deucalion, son of Prometheus, and Pyrrha, daughter of Epimetheus and Pandora. During a visit with his father, Deucalion had been warned about the coming flood. Prometheus told Deucalion to build a large wooden chest, to store meat and drink in it, and to get inside with Pyrrha. They did this and shut themselves in.

They bumped about inside the floating chest for nine days and nights. Finally the chest washed up on Mount Parnassus. They cautiously opened the lid and climbed out. Water swirled all around the rocky peak. In the waves they could see pieces of wood that had once been houses, fences, and wagons. An overturned rowboat floated by, but nowhere was there a sign of life. Both knelt down and thanked the gods for having spared them.

When Zeus saw this, he was so pleased that he sent the streams and rivers back to their channels, and the lakes and oceans back to their beds, and let the two live. Deucalion and Pyrrha started to walk across the lifeless earth. They came to a deserted temple of Themis, the Titan goddess of justice. They prayed to Themis to tell them how to bring life back to the earth.

A voice spoke to them and said, "Go out of my temple and throw the bones of your mother over your shoulders."

They went out of the temple. "I don't understand," said Pyrrha. "Our mothers are buried far from here, and, anyway, it is wrong to disturb the dead."

Deucalion looked about him. Lonely though it was, he was glad to feel the solid earth beneath his feet and to see the land stretch away to the horizon. "Why, the earth is our mother," he said suddenly. He picked up a large gray stone, and pointed to the other stones around them. "And these are her bones."

They began to walk along, throwing stones over their shoulders. Those thrown by Pyrrha turned into women, and those thrown by Deucalion turned into men. And these became the new race of mankind.

QUESTIONS FOR DISCUSSION

1. Does this story remind you of another? How did Deucalion and Pyrrha resemble Noah and his wife? Why did Zeus decide to spare them?
2. Was there ever a time when much of the earth was covered by water? What do scientists know about it? Find out what you can from your library, and see if there is an explanation for what happened.
3. Try diagraming the events in this narrative. Note that everything moves toward the flooding, and then away from it. What, then, is the *turning point?*

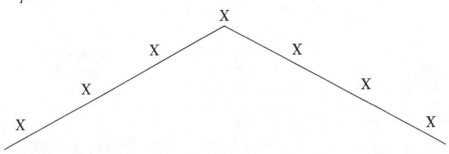

4. Why do you think Zeus is so often portrayed as being rash, given to sudden judgments, quick to anger, prone to act first and think later? Just what do you think Zeus represents? Did the world which the Greeks knew justify a belief in Zeus as kind, understanding, and merciful?
5. Why do you think Prometheus keeps on giving man another chance?
6. What is *your* attitude toward Zeus? Toward Prometheus? Toward the men and women who mistreated Zeus?

Understanding Words

A Common Suffix -ly

   "Zeus behaved *rashly* more often than wisely." What does *rashly* mean? Notice that the word answers the question "How did Zeus behave?" This is a manner adverb, and as you may know, a manner adverb often ends with the suffix -*ly*. Can you think of other examples?

SUGGESTED ACTIVITIES

1. Imagine that *you* met Zeus disguised as a tired old traveler walking along some street. Report the conversation you might carry on with him. Do you think he might feel like throwing one of his famous thunderbolts at mankind today? Why? Why not?

*Deucalion
and the Flood*

2. You know something about several gods and goddesses now. Considering what you already know about Hera, what do you think her reaction would have been toward the destruction of man? Write an imaginary conversation among Hera, Zeus, and Prometheus in which you reveal each of their attitudes. As you read over your dialogue, ask yourself if you have revealed *your* attitude toward man's destruction as well. In what ways?

GREEK HEROES

The myths you have just read are, for the most part, stories about gods and goddesses. Now you will read some tales of Greek heroes whose strength, courage, and wit rival these same attributes in the gods themselves. As you read, note how similar the story patterns are. Each myth is organized around a journey, or a quest of some sort. This journey *motif* (or device for organizing a narrative) is very common, not only in myths but in many other forms of literature. Keep an eye out for it both here and in the unit that follows.

It is possible that Heracles will strike a sympathetic chord with some of you, for as a lad he was far more interested in athletics than in his studies. In fact, he grew so skillful at his chosen field of endeavor that he made a career of it. As you read this tale of mythology's mightiest hero, watch for a narrative pattern to develop.

The Labors of Heracles

Robert Graves

Heracles, whom the Romans called Hercules, was Zeus's son by Alcmene, a Theban princess. Hera, angry that Zeus had made another of his marriages with a mortal woman, sent two tremendous snakes to kill Heracles while still a baby. He and his twin brother Iphicles were lying asleep in a shield, used as a cradle, when the snakes crawled hissing towards them across the floor. Iphicles screamed and rolled out of the shield. But Heracles, an immensely strong child, caught the snakes by their throats, one in each hand, and strangled them.

As a boy, Heracles took far more interest in fighting than in reading, writing, or music; he also preferred roast meat and barley bread to honey cakes and fruit pies. Soon he became the best archer, the best wrestler, and the best boxer alive. Because Linus, his music teacher, beat him for not taking enough trouble over his scales, Heracles knocked Linus dead with a lyre. Accused of murder, Heracles said simply: "Linus hit me first. All I did was to defend myself." The judges let him off.

Eurystheus, the High King of Greece, wanted to banish Amphitryon, King of Thebes, now Heracles's stepfather; but Heracles nobly offered to be his slave for ninety-nine months if Amphitryon might stay and keep his throne. Hera advised Eurystheus: "Agree, but set Heracles the ten most dangerous Labors you can possibly choose, all to be performed in those ninety-nine months. I want him killed."

The First Labor which Eurystheus set Heracles was to kill the Nemean Lion, an enormous beast, with a skin proof against stone, brass, or iron. It lived in a mountain cave. When the arrows which Heracles shot at the lion bounced off harmlessly, he took his great club of wild olive wood and hit it on the head, but only smashed the club. The lion shook its head, because of the singing noise in its ears, then yawned and went back to its cave. This cave had two entrances. Heracles netted the smaller with a brass net and, going in by the larger, caught the lion by the throat. Though it bit off the middle finger of his left hand, he managed to get its head under his right arm and squeeze it to death. Heracles skinned the lion by using one of its own claws for a knife, and afterwards wore the skin. Then he cut himself a second club of wild olive wood and reported to Eurystheus.

The Second Labor was far more dangerous: to kill the monstrous Hydra in the marshes of Lerna. She had a huge body, like a dog's, and eight snake heads on long necks. Heracles fired flaming arrows at the Hydra as she came out from her hole under the roots of a plane tree. Then he rushed forward and battered at the eight heads. As fast as he crushed them, others grew in their places. Up scuttled a crab, sent by Hera, and bit his foot; Heracles broke its shell with a kick. At the same time he drew his sharp, gold-hilted sword and called for Iolaus, his chariot driver. Iolaus hurriedly brought a torch and, after Heracles had cut off each head, singed the neck to prevent a new one from sprouting. That was the end of the Hydra.

Hercules Fights the Amazons

Heracles dipped his arrows in her poisonous blood. Whoever they struck would die painfully.

The Third Labor was to capture the Ceryneian Hind, a white deer with brass hooves and golden horns, belonging to the Goddess Artemis. It took Heracles a whole year to catch the hind. He chased her up hill and down dale all over Greece, until at last he shot an unpoisoned arrow at her as she ran past him; the arrow went between the sinew and bone of her forelegs, without drawing a drop of blood, and pinned them together. As she stumbled and fell, Heracles seized her, drew out the arrow, and carried her on his shoulders to Eurystheus. Artemis would have been furious if he had killed her pet hind, but forgave him because she admired his clever shooting. Eurystheus then set the hind free.

The Fourth Labor was to capture the Erymanthian Boar, a huge creature with tusks like an elephant's, and an arrow-proof skin. Heracles chased it to and fro across the mountains in winter, until it stuck in a deep snowdrift. There he jumped in after it and tied its hind legs to its forelegs. When Eurystheus saw Heracles carrying the boar on his back up the palace avenue, he ran off and hid in a big brass jar.

The Fifth Labor was to clean King Augeias's filthy cattle yard in a single day. Augeias owned many thousands of cattle and never troubled to get rid of the messes they made. Eurystheus set this task just to annoy Heracles, hoping that he would cover himself with filth as he loaded the

dung in baskets and carried them away. Augeias stood and sneered at Heracles: "I bet you twenty cows to one, that you cannot clean the yard in a day."

"Done," said Heracles.

He swung his club, knocked down the yard wall, then borrowed a mattock and quickly dug deep channels from two nearby rivers. The river water, rushing through the yard, washed it clean in a very short time.

As his Sixth Labor, Eurystheus told Heracles to free the Stymphalian Marsh of its brass-feathered, man-eating birds. They looked like cranes, but had beaks that would pierce an iron breastplate. Heracles could not swim through the marsh because it was too muddy, nor walk across it because the mud would not bear his weight; and when he shot at the birds his arrows glanced off their feathers.

The Goddess Athene appeared and handed him a brass rattle. "Shake that!" she ordered. Heracles shook the rattle. The birds rose into the air, mad with terror. He shot and killed scores of them, as they flew off towards the Black Sea; for they had no brass feathers on the undersides of their bodies. None ever returned.

The Seventh Labor was to capture a bull, the terror of Crete. It chased farmers and soldiers, battered down huts and barns, trampled cornfields flat, frightened women and children. This bull had first appeared when Europa's son Minos told the Cretans: "I am King of this island. Let

The Labors of Heracles

the gods send me a sign to prove it!" As he spoke, the Cretans saw a snow-white bull with golden horns swimming in from the sea. But instead of sacrificing this beautiful beast to the gods, as he should have done, Minos kept it and sacrificed another. Zeus punished him by letting the bull escape and make trouble all over Crete.

Heracles tracked the bull to a wood. There he climbed a tree, waited for it to pass, and jumped on its back. After a hard struggle he managed to clip a ring through the bull's nose and take it safely across the sea to Eurystheus.

The Eighth Labor was to capture the four savage mares of the Thracian King Diomedes. Diomedes fed these mares on the flesh of strangers who visited his kingdom. Heracles sailed to Thrace, landed near the palace, went straight to Diomedes's stables, chased away the grooms, and drove the mares plunging and kicking down to the seashore. Alarmed by the noise, Diomedes called the palace guards and hurried in pursuit. Heracles left the mares in charge of his groom Abderus and turned to fight. The battle was short. He stunned Diomedes with his club, and allowed the mares to eat him alive—as they had unfortunately also eaten Abderus, who could not control them. Before he left, Heracles instituted annual funeral games in Abderus's honor. But finding his ship too small for all four mares, he harnessed them to Diomedes's chariot, left the ship behind, and drove home by way of Macedonia.

The Ninth Labor was to get a famous golden girdle from Hippolyte, Queen of the Amazons, who lived on the southern coast of the Black Sea, and bring it back as a present for Eurystheus's daughter. Heracles reached Amazonia without danger. There Queen Hippolyte fell in love with him, and he could have had the girdle as a gift. However, the Goddess Hera spitefully disguised herself as an Amazon and spread the rumor that Heracles had come to kidnap Hippolyte and carry her away to Greece. The angry Amazons jumped on their horses and rode to rescue her, shooting arrows at Heracles as they went. Though Heracles beat off the attack, Hippolyte got killed in the confusion of battle; so he took the girdle from her dead body, and sailed sadly away. He would have liked to marry Hippolyte, and hated giving the girdle to Eurystheus's daughter.

The Tenth Labor was to steal a herd of red cows from King Geryon (who lived on an island near the Ocean Stream). Geryon had three bodies, but only one pair of legs. Hera hoped that Heracles would fail in this last Labor, or else not have time to finish it before the ninety-nine months were up. When he reached the western end of the Mediterranean

Sea, where Spain and Africa were joined together in those days, he cut a channel between them; the cliffs on either side are still called "The Pillars of Heracles." Then he sailed out into the Ocean in a golden boat lent him by the Sun, using his lion-skin for a sail. As he landed on Geryon's island, a two-headed dog attacked him; he struck it dead with a swing of his club, and did the same to Geryon's herdsman. Lastly, Geryon himself rushed from his palace, like a row of three men. The Goddess Hera tried to help him by flashing a mirror in Heracles's eyes, but he dodged and killed Geryon with an arrow shot sideways through all his three bodies. Then he shot at Hera, too, wounding her in the shoulder. She flew off, screaming for Apollo and Artemis to draw out the arrow and make her well again.

Heracles drove the red cows across the Pyrenees and along the south coast of France. At the Alps, however, a messenger of Hera's misdirected him, on purpose. He turned right and went all the way down to the Straits of Messina before he realized that this was Italy, not Greece. Angrily he turned back, and wasted still more time when he reached what is now Trieste, because Hera sent her gadfly, which stung the cows in their tenderest parts. They stampeded eastward, and Heracles had to follow their tracks for five or six hundred miles, as far as the Crimea. There an ugly, snaked-tailed woman promised to round them up, on condition that he kissed her three times. He did so, though grudging every kiss, and at last came safely home to Greece with the cows, just as the ninety-nine months ended.

Heracles should now have been set free but, on Hera's advice, Eurystheus said "You did not perform my Second Labor properly, because you called in your friend Iolaus to help kill the Hydra. And you did not perform my Fifth Labor properly either, because Augeias paid you for cleaning his cattle yard."

"How unfair!" cried Heracles. "I called Iolaus because Hera interfered: she sent a crab to bite my foot. And though Augeias certainly betted me twenty cows to one that I could not clean the cattle yard in a day, I would have performed the Labor anyhow."

"No argument, please! You made the bet; so instead of working for me alone, you got twenty cows from another man."

"Nonsense! Augeias refused to pay me. He claimed that I had not cleaned the yard myself—the River-god did it."

"He was quite right. The Labor should not count as your own work. You must perform two more, but you may take your time over them."

"Agreed," said Heracles, "and if I live to complete them, it will be the worse for your family."

Eurystheus had thought of two very dangerous extra Labors. The first was to fetch the Golden Apples of the Hesperides from the Far West. These apples were the fruit of a tree once given by Mother Earth to Hera as a wedding present. The Hesperides, the Titan Atlas's daughters, tended the tree; and Ladon, an unsleeping dragon, coiled around it.

Heracles visited the Caucasus to ask Prometheus's advice. Prometheus welcomed him, saying: "Please, drive off that vulture. It prevents me from thinking clearly." Heracles not only drove away the vulture, but shot it dead and begged Zeus to forgive Prometheus. Zeus, who felt that the punishment had lasted quite long enough, kindly allowed Heracles to break the chains. However, he ordered Prometheus always to wear an iron finger ring, as a reminder of his slavery. This was how rings first came into fashion.

Prometheus now warned Heracles not to pick the apples himself, because any mortal who did so would drop dead at once. "Persuade some immortal to pick them for you," he suggested. After a farewell feast, Heracles sailed toward Morocco. On reaching Tangier, he walked inland to where Atlas, the rebellious Titan, was holding up the Heavens. Heracles asked: "If I take on your duty for an hour, will you be willing to pick me three apples from your daughters' tree?"

"Certainly," said Atlas, "if you first kill the unsleeping dragon."

Heracles drew his bow and shot Ladon over the garden wall. Then he stood behind Atlas and, straddling his legs wide apart, took the weight of the Heavens on his own head and shoulders. Atlas climbed the wall, greeted his daughters, stole the apples, and shouted to Heracles: "Be good enough to stay there just a little longer, while I carry these apples to Eurystheus. With my huge legs I should be back here in an hour's time."

Though Heracles knew that Atlas would never deliver the apples, but go off to rescue the other Titans instead, and start a new rebellion, he pretended to trust him. "With pleasure," he answered, "if you will please take the weight from me again for one moment more, while I fold up this lion-skin to make a comfortable head pad."

Atlas laid down the apples and did as Heracles asked. Heracles then took the apples and walked away. "You tried to trick me," he said, laughing, "but I have tricked you. Goodbye!"

As Heracles went home through Libya, a gigantic son of Mother Earth, by name Antaeus, challenged him to a wrestling match. Heracles oiled himself all over, so that Antaeus could not get a firm grip of him; Antaeus, on the contrary, rubbed himself with sand. Every time Heracles threw Antaeus hard to the ground, he was surprised to see him rise again stronger than ever because touching Mother Earth renewed his strength. Realizing what he must do, Heracles lifted Antaeus off the ground, cracked his ribs, and held him aloft out of Mother Earth's reach, until he died. A month later Heracles brought the apples safely to Eurystheus.

The last and worst Labor was to capture the dog Cerberus, and drag him up from Tartarus. On receiving this order, Heracles went for purification to Eleusis, where Demeter's Mysteries were held, and now cleansed of all defilement boldly descended to Tartarus. Charon refused to ferry a live mortal across the Styx.

"I will wreck your boat," Heracles threatened, "and fill you as full of arrows as a hedgehog is full of prickles."

Charon shivered in terror and ferried him across. Hades afterwards punished Charon for his cowardice.

Heracles saw Theseus and Peirithous stuck to Hades's bench, and being whipped by the Furies. He gave Theseus an enormous tug and wrenched him free, though a large part of his back stayed behind. But finding it impossible to release Peirithous, except with an axe, he left him there.

Persephone darted from the palace and took Heracles by both hands. "Can I help you, dear Heracles?" she asked.

"Be kind enough to lend me your watchdog for a few days, Your Majesty. He can run home again as soon as I have shown him to Eurystheus."

Persephone turned to King Hades: "Please, Husband, grant Heracles what he asks. This is a task set him on your sister-in-law Hera's advice. He promises not to keep our dog Cerberus."

Hades answered: "Very well, and he may take that fool Theseus back, too, while he is about it. Still, I must make it a rule that he masters Cerberus without the use of club or arrows."

Hades thought this a safe condition, but Heracles's lion-skin was proof against the blows of Cerberus's barbed tail; and his strong hands squeezed Cerberus's throat until all three heads turned black. Cerberus fainted, and let himself be dragged up on earth. Unfortunately, the only tunnel wide enough for him was one that came out near Mariandyne, beside the Black Sea; so Heracles had a long and difficult journey. Before starting, he took a branch of the white poplar with him for a trophy, and wore it as a wreath.

Eurystheus was nearly scared to death when Heracles appeared, dragging Cerberus behind him on a leash. "Thank you, noble Heracles," he said, "you are now free of your Labors. But please send that brute back at once."

Heracles returned to Thebes, where his mother Alcmene welcomed him joyfully. Then Hera thought of a clever plot. She told Autolycus to steal a herd of dappled mares and foals from a man named Iphitus, change their color, and sell them to Heracles. Iphitus tracked the herd all the way to Tiryns by their footprints, and asked Heracles whether he had taken them by any chance. Heracles led Iphitus to the top of a high tower, and said, grimly: "Look around you! Can you see any dappled mares in my pastures?"

"No," answered Iphitus. "But I know that they are somewhere about."

Heracles, losing his temper at being thought a thief and a liar, flung Iphitus over the battlements.

The gods sentenced Heracles to be the slave of Queen Omphale of Lydia; the money he fetched at his sale, which Hermes had arranged, went to Iphitus's orphan children. Omphale, who did not know who Heracles was, asked him what he could do. "Anything you like, madam," he answered readily. So she made him dress as a woman, in a yellow petticoat, handed him a distaff, and showed him how to spin wool. Heracles found the work very restful. One day a gigantic dragon started eating Omphale's Lydian subjects, and she said to Heracles: "You look a strong man. Dare you fight the dragon?"

"At your service, madam."

Dragons were nothing to Heracles. He shot a poisoned arrow between this dragon's jaws, and Omphale gratefully gave him his freedom.

Later, Heracles married a princess named Deianeira, a daughter of the God Dionysus, and founded the Olympic Games, which were to be held every four years as long as the world should last. He ruled that the winners of each event were to be given wreaths, instead of the usual valuable prizes, because he had not been paid for his Labors either. No man dared wrestle against Heracles, which disappointed the spectators. However, King Zeus kindly came down from Olympus. He and Heracles had a wonderful tussle together. The match ended in a draw, and everyone cheered.

Heracles now took vengeance on kings who had treated him scornfully while he was performing his Labors, including Augeias, and killed three of Eurystheus's sons. Zeus forbade him to attack Eurystheus himself. That would set a bad example to other freed slaves. The River-god Achelous challenged Heracles to a fight, but lost a horn in the struggle. Heracles also fought the God Ares and sent him hobbling back to Olympus.

One day a Centaur named Nessus offered to carry Heracles's wife, Deianeira, across a flooded river for a small fee. Heracles paid the money, but Nessus, having reached the farther bank, galloped off with Deianeira in his arms. Heracles shot Nessus, at a distance of half a mile, using one of the arrows dipped in the Hydra's blood. The dying Nessus whispered to Deianeira: "Collect a little of my blood in this small oil jar. Then, if Heracles ever loves another woman more than you, here is a sure charm to use. The oil will keep my blood from drying up. Spread it on his shirt. He will never be unfaithful again. Goodbye!" Deianeira did as Nessus advised.

While still serving Eurystheus, Heracles had taken part in an archery contest proposed by King Eurytus of Oechalia, the prize of which was his daughter Iole. Eurytus boasted himself the best archer in Greece, and felt very cross at being beaten by Heracles. He shouted: "My daughter is a princess. I cannot possibly marry her to Eurystheus's slave. The competition is void." Remembering this insult some years later, Heracles sacked Oechalia, killed Eurytus, and took away Iole, with her two sisters, to scrub floors and cook. Deianeira feared that he might fall in love with Iole, who

was very beautiful. When he sent a messenger home, asking Deianeira for his best embroidered shirt, she thought: "He wants to wear it when he marries Iole." So she smeared some of Nessus's blood on the red embroidering of the shirt, where it would not show, and handed it to the messenger.

Heracles really needed the shirt for a thanksgiving sacrifice to Zeus, after the capture of Oechalia. He put it on, and was pouring wine on the altar when he suddenly felt as though he were being bitten by scorpions. The heat of his body had melted the Hydra's poison in Nessus's blood. He yelled, bellowed, shrieked, knocked over the altar, and tried to rip off the shirt; but great lumps of flesh came away too. His blood hissed with the poison. Then he jumped into a stream; the poison burned him worse than before. Heracles knew that he was doomed.

He begged his friends in an unsteady voice: "Please, carry me to Mount Oeta, and build a pyre of oak and wild-olive." They obeyed, weeping. Heracles climbed to the platform at the top, and calmly lay down on his lion-skin, using his club for a pillow. He let himself be burned to death; the fire hurt far less than the Hydra's poison.

Zeus felt proud of his brave son. He told the Olympians: "Heracles will be our porter, and marry my daughter Hebe, the Goddess of Youth. If anyone objects, I shall start throwing thunderbolts. Rise, noble soul of Heracles! Welcome to Olympus!"

Zeus looked so fierce that Hera dared say nothing. Heracles's immortal soul ascended on a cloud, and Athene was soon introducing him to the other gods. Only Ares turned his back, but when Demeter begged him not to be a fool he too shook hands with Heracles—rather rudely.

Deianeira, hearing that she had caused Heracles's death, took a sword and stabbed herself.

QUESTIONS FOR DISCUSSION

1. Why does Hera dislike young Heracles? Although there are a series of conflicts in this tale, what is the basic conflict?
2. You might think of this narrative as assuming the form of a road which is filled with hefty stones. Heracles goes up and over and on to the next obstruction, in an almost endless succession of mighty labors. Yet each labor has a miniature narrative pattern within it. Look carefully at the action of each labor. Are there usually several failures, or thwarted attempts, before the hero is successful? How does this heighten suspense?

3. Sometimes in the folk narrative (fable, myth, and folktale) we can spot an obvious device used by the teller to keep the action going. After Heracles finished his ninety-nine months, he was supposed to be free. What happened?
4. Heracles's final labor was a trip to the underworld. In what way does this resemble the story of Zeus you studied earlier? Does it remind you of any other myth?
5. Jealousy of the gods had created Heracles's problems. How did human jealousy end them?
6. The beginning of this story is quite long. What useful purpose does it fulfill?
7. What does the middle part of the story consist of? Do you think that all of these episodes were originally told at one sitting? Could other episodes be included? Does this remind you of a popular form of entertainment today? Explain.
8. How did the story end? Was it the kind of ending you expected?
9. Do you suppose the Greeks believed every word of these stories? What was the purpose of the exaggeration?
10. The stories of Heracles all tell about the wonderful strength of this popular hero. What other subjects do they deal with, on the deeper level of ideas?
11. Why do you suppose Heracles was made a god after his death? Can you think of other examples of heroes who have become immortalized, if not worshiped?
12. Are these stories about Heracles written in the same impersonal style as the creation myths, or do you know how the teller of the story feels about certain characters?

Understanding Words

A Vocabulary Quiz

Answer *Yes* or *No* to the following questions.

1. Could you kill a lion, whose skin was *proof* against stone, brass, or iron, by stabbing it through the heart with a dagger?
2. Could Heracles have *singed* the neck of the monstrous Hydra with a rock?
3. Could you dig a trench with a *mattock?*
4. Would you use soap and water for *purification?*
5. Is *defilement* the "what is left" after filing something?
6. Would Cerberus's *barbed* tail be smooth to touch?
7. Would a *trophy* be a useful thing to have in the kitchen?

The Labors of Heracles

Have you ever looked at the constellation of stars known as the Lyre? Those stars were named for a musical instrument (a kind of harp) that once belonged to a young poet and musician named Orpheus. He sang so beautifully that he brought tears to the iron face of King Hades of the underworld, but Fate held a cruel destiny for him. We remember him in other ways, as well. *Orphean* still means melodiously enchanting. In more recent times, music halls, vaudeville houses, and movie theaters have been named "Orpheum" in his honor.

Orpheus

Robert Graves

Orpheus's mother was Calliope, one of the Nine Muses, and she inspired poets. Besides being a poet, Orpheus played the lyre so well that he could not only tame wild beasts with his music, but make rocks and trees move from their places to follow him. One unlucky day his beautiful wife Eurydice trod on a sleeping snake, which woke and bit her. She died of the poison, so Orpheus boldly went down to Tartarus, playing his lyre, to fetch her away. He charmed Charon into ferrying him across the Styx without payment; he charmed Cerberus into whining and licking his feet; he charmed the Furies into laying down their whips and listening to him, while all punishments ceased; he charmed Queen Persephone into giving him the secret password for the Pool of Memory; he even charmed King Hades into freeing Eurydice and letting her follow him up on earth again. Hades made only one condition: that Orpheus must not look behind him until Eurydice was safely back in the sunlight. So he went off, singing and playing happily. Eurydice followed; but at the last minute Orpheus feared that Hades might be tricking him, forgot the condition, looked anxiously behind him—and lost her forever.

When Zeus made his son Dionysus an Olympian, Orpheus refused to worship the new god, whom he accused of setting mortals a bad example by his wild behavior. Dionysus angrily ordered a crowd of Maenads—drunken young women—to chase Orpheus. They caught him without his lyre, cut off his head, which they threw into a river, and tore him into little pieces. The Nine Muses sadly collected these and buried them at the foot of Mount Olympus, where the nightingales ever afterwards sang more sweetly than anywhere else. Orpheus's head floated singing down the river to the sea, and fishermen rescued it for burial on the island of Lemnos. Zeus then let Apollo put Orpheus's lyre in the sky as the constellation still called the Lyre.

QUESTIONS FOR DISCUSSION

1. Can you discover the beginning, middle, and end pattern in this narrative?
2. Orpheus was Apollo's son, and his mother was one of the Nine Muses. Why was it not surprising that he became a poet?
3. Is the author noncommittal about the fate of Orpheus? How do you feel about his fate? Why did Zeus feel he merited such punishment? What did you learn anything about the young poet besides that he could sing well? How did you find these things out?

He may not have been as successful as the Wright Brothers were one day to be, but Daedalus was perhaps the first man to attempt flight. He was a wonderfully skilled mechanic, able to build all sorts of unusual and delightful things. That, in fact, was his chief trouble: he was *too* clever.

Daedalus

Robert Graves

Woodcut,
by Albrecht Dürer

Daedalus, the Athenian, a wonderfully skillful smith taught by Athene and Hephaestus, grew jealous of his nephew Talus and killed him. Talus, though only twelve years old, had invented the saw, which he copied in brass from the teeth of a snake. To avoid being hanged, Daedalus fled to Crete, where King Minos, Europa's son, welcomed him. Minos was short of good workmen. Daedalus married a Cretan girl, by whom he had a son named Icarus; and made Minos all sorts of statues, furniture, machines,

Daedalus

57

weapons, armor, and toys for the palace children. After some years he asked for a month's holiday, and when Minos said: "Certainly not!" decided to escape.

He knew it would be useless to steal a boat and sail away, because Minos's fast ships would soon overtake him. So he made himself and Icarus a pair of wings each, to strap on their arms. The big quills he threaded to a frame; but the smaller feathers were held together by bees-wax. Having helped Icarus on with his pair of wings, Daedalus warned him: "Be careful not to fly too low, my boy, for fear of the sea spray; or too high, for fear of the sun."

Daedalus flew off, Icarus followed; but presently soared so near the sun that the wax melted and the feathers came unstuck. Icarus lost height, fell into the sea and drowned.

Daedalus buried his son's body on a small island, later called Icaria, where the sea had washed it up; then sadly flew on to the court of King Cocalus in Sicily. Minos pursued him by ship, but Daedalus begged the Sicilians not to reveal his hiding place. However, the clever Minos took a large triton shell, and offered a bag of gold to anyone who could pass a linen thread through all the shell's whorls, and out through a tiny hole at the very top. When he came to Cocalus's palace, Cocalus, anxious to win the reward, took the shell indoors and asked Daedalus to solve the problem for him. "That is easy," said Daedalus. "Tie the gossamer from a spider's web to the hind-leg of an ant, put the ant into the shell, and then smear honey around the hole at the top. The ant will smell the honey and go circling up all the whorls in search of it. As soon as the ant reappears, catch it, tie a woman's hair to the other end of the gossamer, and pull it carefully through. Then tie a linen thread to the end of the hair, and pull that through as well."

Cocalus followed his advice. Minos, seeing the threaded shell, paid him the gold, but said sternly: "Only Daedalus could have thought of this! I shall burn your palace to the ground, unless you give him up."

Cocalus promised to do so, and invited Minos to take a warm bath in the new bathroom built by Daedalus. But Cocalus's daughters, to save their friend—who had given them a set of beautiful dolls, with moveable arms and legs—poured boiling water down the bathroom pipe instead of warm, and scalded Minos to death. Cocalus pretended that Minos had died by accident: tripping over the bath mat and falling into the tub before cold water could be added. Fortunately the Cretans believed this story.

1. Myths sometimes attempt to explain the origin of things, as we have already seen. What seems to be the subject of this myth? Does it differ from the earlier ones you have read? In what way?
2. Usually Greek heroes were exceedingly strong and brave, for these were two virtues deeply admired by the Greeks. Daedalus, however, has another talent. What is it? How does he use it to outwit his enemies?
3. Note that the action in this myth is neatly divided into two parts. Daedalus fled his homeland, and found refuge in Crete. How do events repeat themselves in the latter part of the story? Did you find any repetitive patterns in the earlier myths? Give examples.

"Pride goeth before a fall," as you know. Poor Bellerophon! He had just cause for pride. What horse could ever match the splendid Pegasus? As you read this myth, see if you can detect some of the elements of another type of folk narrative. Do you see any resemblance to the fable here?

Bellerophon

Robert Graves

Bellerophon of Corinth was engaged to marry the princess Aethra, but accidentally killed a man in a dart-throwing competition and had to leave the country. He fled to the town of Tiryns, where the King invited him to be his guest. The Queen fell in love with Bellerophon, caught hold of him on the stairs, and said: "Darling, let us run away together!"

"Certainly not!" exclaimed Bellerophon. "You are married, and the King has been very kind to me."

The Queen went to the King and whispered spitefully in his ear: "That rascal Bellerophon has just asked me to run away with him. Did you ever hear of such shocking behavior?"

The King believed the story, but dared not offend the Furies by killing his guest. Instead, he wrote a letter to his father-in-law Iobates, the King of Lycia in Asia Minor, and sent Bellerophon across the sea with it. The letter, which was sealed, read: "Please behead the bearer of this. He has been very rude to my Queen, your daughter."

Bellerophon

59

King Iobates dared not offend Hermes, the God of Travelers and Messengers, by beheading Bellerophon. Instead, he asked him to kill the Chimaera. This chimaera was a fire-breathing goat with a lion's head and snake's tail, which guarded the palace of Iobates's enemy, the King of Caria.

Bellerophon promised to do his best. He prayed to the Goddess Athene, who advised him first to tame a wild winged horse called Pegasus, living on Mount Helicon, which the Muses fed in winter when snow covered the grass. Bellerophon knew that Pegasus often flew south to the Isthmus of Corinth; and had once or twice seen him drinking at a favorite spring there. So Bellerophon revisited Corinth in secret — being afraid that he might be arrested for murder; and prayed to Athene again. Athene brought him a golden bridle, with which he waited all night behind a rock near the spring, until at dawn, by good luck, Pegasus flew down to drink. Quickly Bellerophon threw the bridle over Pegasus's head, and tamed him after a fierce struggle.

At that moment, Bellerophon's enemies came up to arrest him; but he mounted Pegasus and flew away to Caria. There he circled above the palace until he saw the Chimaera blowing fire in the courtyard beneath, and shot her full of arrows. But he could not kill the monster, until he stuck a lump of lead on the point of a spear and pushed it into her open jaws. The fiery breath melted the lead: it trickled down her throat and burned holes in her stomach. So died the Chimaera.

Afterwards, Iobates gave Bellerophon several other important tasks. Bellerophon behaved with such courage and modesty on every occasion, that at last Iobates showed him the letter from Tiryns, and said: "Tell me, is this true?" When Bellerophon explained what had really happened, Iobates cried: "There! My eldest daughter was always a liar, and I apologize for believing the story." Then he married Bellerophon to his younger daughter, who was both well-behaved and beautiful, and in his will left him the throne of Lycia.

Bellerophon grew very proud. He stupidly tried to call on the Olympians in their palace, without having been invited. He rode through the air on Pegasus, dressed in crown and robes. Zeus, seeing him from a long way off, shouted: "A curse on this impudent mortal! Hera, my dear, please send a gadfly to sting Pegasus under the tail!" Hera did so. Pegasus reared, and Bellerophon tumbled off. He fell half a mile, bounced off the side of a river valley, and rolled down a slope into a thorn bush. After that, his fate was to wander about the earth under Zeus's curse: lame, poor, and deserted by his friends. But Zeus caught Pegasus and used him as a pack-horse to carry thunderbolts.

1. Is the subject of this myth two-fold? If so, can you state the dual subjects?
2. In what way are the opening incidents in "Daedalus" similar to the beginning of this myth? Are there other obvious similarities? What are they?
3. Diagram the action in this story, separating the incidents into the familiar beginning, middle, and end pattern. Does this help you to understand the subject? In what way?

When he was only fifteen, Perseus set out bravely to slay Medusa, the dreadful gorgon, with snakes entwined in her hair and the power to turn to stone whomever looked into her eyes. You will find young Perseus one of the most likable of all the Greek heroes. As you read this tale, see if it is in any way similar to some of the others you have read.

Perseus

Robert Graves

An oracle had warned Acrisius, King of Argos, that his grandson would kill him. "Then I shall take care to have no grandchildren," Acrisius grunted. Going home, he locked Danaë, his only daughter, in a tower with brass doors, guarded by a savage dog, and brought all her food with his own hands.

Zeus fell in love with Danaë when he saw her, from far off, leaning sadly over the battlements. To disguise himself from Hera, Zeus became a shower of golden rain and descended on the tower. Danaë hurried downstairs, the rain trickled after her, and then Zeus changed back into his own shape. "Will you marry me?" he asked Danaë.

"Yes, she answered, "I am very lonely here."

A son was born to her. She named him Perseus. Hearing a baby cry behind the brass door, Acrisius grew furious.

"Who is your husband?"

"The God Zeus, Father. Dare to touch your grandchild, and Zeus will strike you dead!"

"Then I will put you both out of his reach."

Acrisius locked Danaë and Perseus in a wooden chest, with a basket of food and a bottle of wine, and threw the chest into the sea. "If they drown, it will be Poseidon's fault, not mine," he told his courtiers.

Zeus ordered Poseidon to take particular care of the chest. Poseidon kept the sea calm, and presently a fisherman from the island of Seriphos saw the chest floating on the water. He caught it with his net and towed it ashore. When he knocked off the lid, out stepped Danaë, unhurt, carrying Perseus in her arms.

The friendly fisherman took them to Polydectes, King of Seriphos, who at once offered to marry Danaë. "That cannot be," she said. "I am already married to Zeus."

"I daresay, but if Zeus may have two wives, why not have two husbands yourself?"

"Gods do as they please. Mortals may marry only one wife or husband at a time."

Polydectes constantly tried to make Danaë change her mind. She always shook her head, saying: "If I married you, Zeus would kill us both!"

When Perseus was fifteen years old, Polydectes called him and said: "Since your mother will not be my Queen, I shall marry a princess on the Greek mainland. I am asking each of my subjects to give me a· horse, because her father needs fifty of them as a marriage fee. Will you oblige?"

Perseus answered: "I have no horse, Your Majesty, nor any money to buy one. However, if you promise to marry that princess and stop pestering my mother, I will give you whatever you want—anything in the world—even Medusa's head."

"Medusa's head will do very well," said Polydectes.

This Medusa had been a beautiful woman whom Athene had once caught kissing Poseidon in her temple. Athene was so angered by his bad manners that she changed Medusa into a gorgon — a winged monster with glaring eyes, huge teeth, and snakes for hair. Whoever looked at her would turn to stone.

Athene helped Perseus by handing him a polished shield to use as a mirror when he cut off Medusa's head, so as not to be turned into stone; and Hermes gave him a sharp sickle. But Perseus still needed the God Hades's helmet of invisibility, also a magic bag in which to put the head, and a pair of winged sandals. All these useful things were guarded by the Naiads of the River Styx.

Perseus went to ask the Three Grey Sisters for the Naiads' secret address. It was difficult enough to find the Three Grey Sisters, who lived near the Garden of the Hesperides, and had only a single eye and a single tooth between them. When Perseus eventually reached their house, he crept up behind them as they passed the eye and the tooth from one to the other. Then he snatched both these treasures and refused to return them until the Grey Sisters gave him the Naiads' address. He found them in a pool under a rock near the entrance of Tartarus, and threatened to tell all the world about them, unless they lent him the helmet, the sandals, and the bag. The Naiads hated anyone to know that, though otherwise good-looking, they had dogs' faces; so they did as Perseus asked.

Perseus, now wearing the helmet and the sandals, flew unseen to Libya. Coming upon Medusa asleep, he looked at her reflexion in the polished shield and cut off her head with his sickle. The only unfortunate accident was that Medusa's blood trickling from the bag, in which the head lay, turned into poisonous snakes as it hit the earth. This made the land of Libya unsafe for ever afterwards. When Perseus stopped to thank the Three Grey Sisters, the Titan Atlas called out: "Tell your father Zeus that unless he frees me pretty soon, I shall let the Heavens fall—which will be the end of the world."

Perseus showed Medusa's head to Atlas, who at once turned to stone, and became the great Mount Atlas.

As he flew on to Palestine, Perseus saw a beautiful princess named Andromeda chained to a rock at Joppa, and a sea-serpent, sent by the God Poseidon, swimming towards her with wide-open jaws. Andromeda's parents, Cepheus and Cassiopeia, the King and Queen of the Philistines, were ordered by an oracle to chain her there as food for the monster. It seems that Cassiopeia had told the Philistines: "I am more beautiful than all the Nereids in the sea"— a boast which angered their proud father, the God Poseidon. Perseus dived at the sea-serpent from above and cut off its head. Afterwards he unchained Andromeda, took her home, and asked permission to marry her. King Cepheus answered: "Impudence! She is already promised to the King of Tyre."

"Then why did the King of Tyre not save her?"

"Because he was afraid to offend Poseidon."

"Well, I feared no one. I killed the monster. Andromeda is mine."

As Perseus spoke, the King of Tyre arrived at the head of his army, shouting: "Away, stranger, or we shall cut you into little pieces!"

Perseus told Andromeda: "Please shut your eyes tight, Princess!"

Andromeda obeyed. He pulled Medusa's head from his bag and turned everyone but Andromeda to stone.

When Perseus flew back to Seriphos, carrying Andromeda in his arms, he found that Polydectes had cheated him after all. Instead of marrying the princess on the mainland, he was still pestering Danaë. Perseus turned him and his whole family to stone, and made the friendly fisherman king of the island. Then he gave Medusa's head to Athene, and asked Hermes would he kindly return the borrowed helmet, bag, and sandals to the Naiads of the Styx? In this way he showed far greater sense than Bellerophon, who had gone on using the winged horse Pegasus after killing the Chimaera. The gods decided that Perseus deserved a long, happy life. They let him marry Andromeda, become King of Tiryns, and build the famous city of Mycenae near by.

As for King Acrisius, Perseus met him one afternoon at an athletic competition. "Good day, Grandfather! My mother Danaë asks me to forgive you. If I disobey her, the Furies will whip me, so you are safe from my vengeance."

Acrisius thanked him, but when Perseus took part in the quoit-throwing competition, a sudden wind caught the quoit he had thrown and sent it crashing through Acrisius's skull. Later, Perseus and Andromeda were turned into constellations, and so were Andromeda's parents, Cepheus and Cassiopeia.

QUESTIONS FOR DISCUSSION

1. What is this myth about? Is it about more than Naiads, monsters, gods, and demi-gods? What other things is it concerned with? Is it concerned with ideas as well? Can you state both subjects?
2. Is there any similarity between the childhood of this hero and that of any of the others you have read about? Explain.
3. Is there a recognizable beginning, middle, and end pattern in this myth? Can you identify the parts?
4. This myth, like others, offers explanations of the origins of places. What explanations are given?
5. What difference can you find between Perseus and Bellerophon?

An Interesting Word, oracle

In ancient Greece, in the temple of Apollo at Delphi, a priestess sat on a tripod placed over a chasm through which sulphurous fumes escaped. Breathing these vapors apparently caused her to undergo some sort of frenzy in which she gave inspired utterances believed to be the voice of the god Apollo. The priests at the temple "translated" these messages to people who came for advice. Often the answers the priests gave to the questions were very ambiguous, and could be understood in more than one way. The advantage of course was that they were always right. A famous example is that of a Lydian ruler who was told that if he crossed a certain river he would destroy an empire. He crossed it, believing the oracle meant that he would destroy his enemy. Unfortunately it was his own empire that was destroyed!

What are some modern "oracles"?

A SUMMING UP

1. You have read a number of myths concerning Greek gods and heroes. Are there any similarities in the subjects? See if you can make a statement about the subject of these myths that would fit any one, or all of them.
2. Zeus as a child was hidden away from his father, who, you recall, had a strange appetite. Think back over the Greek heroes you have read about. Which of them had perilous childhoods?
3. Do myths, as a rule, have a moral, as does the parable? Did any of the myths you read have a moral? If you think so, indicate which ones and try to state the moral of each.
4. Often a Greek hero braved the horrors of the underworld as a climax to his struggles, and returned triumphant. Look at the myths again. Which heroes underwent this ordeal? What could such a trip represent, do you think? Why, in your opinion, was it usually the last or final ordeal the hero suffered?
5. The early Greeks considered physical strength and courage as two of man's greatest virtues. Do you agree? Why, or why not? What other qualities do these heroes possess that you admire? Do they exhibit any that you dislike? What do you learn about the early Greeks from these heroes? What do you learn about man in general?
6. The myth, parable, proverb, and fable are all forms of folk literature. What common characteristics do you think they share? How do they differ? Are they all narratives? Are their subjects similar?

Greek Myths

7. Sometimes stories plunge us immediately into exciting action, and, once the story is completed, end cleanly and abruptly. Is this a characteristic of the myth? Check the various beginnings and endings of the myths you've read. Are we told, for instance, about other things after Heracles dies?

8. Some of the gods — Zeus, for example — appear in several myths. Think back over the various myths. Does Zeus always seem to be the same kind of god in each story? In what ways does he always seem alike? In what ways is he sometimes different?

9. For the most part the Greek heroes seem less fickle, less cruel, and less quarrelsome than do the gods. Can you think of any reason why this should be so? What do the gods seem to symbolize in these stories?

10. Do the tellers of these tales seem to criticize the gods when they act foolishly or in anger? Or are the actions of the gods merely reported, without judgment being passed? Give examples to back up your idea.

11. The first nine myths included here were stories of Greek gods. Compare the subject matter of these with the subjects of the hero tales. Are they different? In what way? Do they have similarities? Explain.

12. You have found that the various types of folk literature you have studied share certain characteristics, although they differ in subject and in form. You have already worked out your own definition for the proverb, the parable, and the fable. Now attempt to define the myth as you understand it.

13. Many words from the Greek myths remain in our language today. If possible, find a book called *Words from the Myths*, by Isaac Asimov, in your library. Read some of the stories that explain how words from mythology have enriched our language. Then write a short paragraph describing some of the explanations you found most interesting. If possible, share this information with your classmates by reading it aloud in class.

SUGGESTED ACTIVITIES

1. The Greek myths are more than fairy tales and adventure stories. They have become part of our culture. The Greeks themselves named the stars and planets after characters in the myths, and we have kept those names. Make a list of some of these names, and find out a little about the character each represents.

2. Scientific language has been influenced by the Greeks. The space program especially has relied upon the Greek myths to provide names for the rockets and missiles that probe the mysteries of outer space. Find out

the names given to these machines, and tell who was the original holder of the name, and, if possible, why the name is appropriate to the machine.

3. In ancient Greece, a religion grew up around the myths, and the literature was filled with it. Find out what you can about the religious observances of the Greeks and prepare a report for the class.

4. *My Fair Lady,* a popular musical show, was based on an old Greek myth called "Pygmalion." Read the original story and explain how the idea was used to create the show. Find other examples in literature, music, or drama in which the idea was borrowed from the Greeks.

5. Producers of goods or services often take their trademarks from mythology. A glance through the yellow pages of the telephone book will supply some — flowers by wire, for example, or gasoline. Find as many as you can, and explain what each name or symbol stands for and why it is appropriate to the thing advertised.

6. Write a myth of your own. It can be an entertaining one, like the Heracles stories, to show how brave, or clever, or powerful a hero is. You may make up your own characters, and they may be as fantastic as you would like to make them. Or, if you prefer, write a myth to explain some puzzling circumstance: What is a rainbow? Why does a peacock have such beautiful feathers? What is thunder? Where do the birds go in winter? You may choose any natural phenomenon as your subject and give an imaginative explanation for it.

7. The ancient Greeks regarded fire as the most important step forward in their civilization, and therefore honored Prometheus who gave the gift to them. What modern discovery do you think has furthered the advance of civilization to an equal extent? Which one of the gods might have been responsible for giving this gift to man? Write a story about how the gift was given, and what the reaction of the gods on Mount Olympus might have been.

8. Read several myths from a supplementary source. Choose one that appeals to you, and retell it to the class in a way that you think will make it interesting to them.

GLOSSARY

Alcmene (alk mē′ nē) Zeus' mortal wife and Heracles' mother.

Aphrodite (af′ rə dī″ tē) Greek goddess of beauty and love

Apollo (ə pol′ lō) handsome god of poetry and music

Ares (âr′ ēz) son of Zeus and Hera

Artemis (är′ tə mis) twin of Apollo, goddess of the moon and hunt

Athena (ə thē′ nə) goddess of knowledge

Greek Myths

Atlas (at′ ləs) Titan condemned to support the heavens with his shoulders

Atlantides (ət lan′ ti dēz) goddesses, daughters of Atlas

Augeias (ȯ jē′ ȧs) King Augeias's stables were cleaned by Heracles

Calliope (kə lī′ ə pē) chief of Muses

Centaurs (sen′ tȯ(ə)rz) creatures pictured as half man and half horse

Cerberus (sərb′ (ə) rəs) three-headed dog who guarded Hades

Chaos (kā′ äs) unordered matter from which the world was created

Charon (ka (a)′ rən) grim ferryman who serviced the River Styx

Cronus (krō′ nəs) most powerful of Titans

Cyclops (sī′ kläps) giants possessing a single, staring eye

Danaë (dan″ ə ē′) mother of Perseus

Deianeira (dē′ yə nī″ rə) beautiful wife of Heracles

Demeter (di mē′ tər) goddess of agriculture

Dionysus (dī′ ə nī″ səs) demigod who became God of the Grapevine

Epimetheus (ep′ ə mē″ thē əs) brother of Prometheus

Eurydice (yu̇ rid″ i sē′) bride of Orpheus

Eurystheus (yu̇ ris′ thē əs) prince whom Heracles had to serve

Gaea (jē′ ə) goddess of the earth

Gorgans (gȯr′ gənz) ugly, monstrous women whose hair was made up of snakes

Hades (hā′ dēz) god of underworld, brother of Zeus

Medusa (mə d(y)ü″ sə) best known of the Gorgons

Menelaus (men′ ə lā″ əs) King of Mycenae

Minos (mī′ nəs) King of Crete

Muses (myüz′ əz) nine daughters of Zeus, goddesses of the various fine arts

Nestor (nes′ tər) King of Pylus

nymph (nim(p)f) any minor Greek goddess pictured as a young girl

Oceanus (ō shē′ an əs) oldest of Titans, who symbolizes water

Pan (pan) a lesser god of field and wood, half goat

Pandora (pan dōr′ ə) beautiful woman

Persephone (pər səf′ ə nē) daughter of Demeter, carried to the underworld by Hades

Perseus (pər′ sē əs) son of Zeus and Danae

Poseidon (pō sīd′ ən) Greek god of the sea

Prometheus (prə mē′ thē əs) a Titan who stole fire from the sun

Rhea (rē′ ə) Titaness, wife of Cronus

Styx (stiks) the river surrounding Hades

Tartarus (tär′ tər əs) the kingdom of Hades

Titans and Titanesses (tīt′ ənz) giant offspring of Uranus and Gaea

Uranus (yu̇ rā′ nəs) Greek god of sky

Zeus (züs) chief of the Olympian gods and goddesses

Norse Myths

The Norsemen, like the Greeks, wondered about the beginning of the world and how man came to be. They too invented stories to explain what they could not understand.

The world of Norse mythology was different in many ways from the Greek. Norsemen thought of the universe as a fairly flat plain surrounded by mist and darkness. Below was the infernal region of Niflheim, a world of mist, cold, and ice.

Norse gods, known as the Aesir, lived in the palace of Asgard. They were great warriors who fought continually in a way which reflected the climate and conditions of the Northland. The world was cold and dark most of the year; bitter winds swept the plains. Men had to combat the harsh climate, and in order to survive they often had to fight each other for a bite of food or a little warmth. The cruel natural forces were reflected in the lives of their gods.

Conflict among the immortals is just as frequent and important in Norse mythology as it was in the Greek myths. Norsemen believed that in time there would be a great struggle between Odin, the ruler of the gods, and his enemies. The gods would be brought to judgment and the world would be destroyed by ice, flood, and fire. After the battle there would be a new heaven and a new earth ruled by the Allfather, who would be greater than the god Odin.

When the Norwegian nobles moved to Iceland many hundreds of years ago, they took with them the songs and traditions about their gods and heroes. The *scald*, or poet, transmitted the myths orally from generation to generation. This poetry described the creation of the world, the relation of the gods to men, the downfall of the gods, and the new heaven and new earth. Later these myths were recorded in the scaldic poems, the *Eddas*—one a collection of myths in poetry, one a collection in prose—and in the sagas, which were short, exciting tales of heroes.

Although there are not as many Norse myths as there are Greek, they are among the finest stories in literature. You will enjoy the adventures of the gods, some involving journeys which require strength, energy, love of life, and cunning. You will admire the courage of these people who believed that victory was possible in death.

Norse Myths

In the beginning, the Greeks said, there was Chaos, and out of Chaos came darkness, light, life, and love. But the Norsemen, surrounded by lonely mountains and bitter cold, had a different belief. In the beginning, there were cold and warmth, with a gap between, and out of the meeting of these two elemental forces the world was created. Can you think of any reasons why the Norsemen envisioned such a creation?

The Creation

Olivia E. Coolidge

Ages ago, the Norsemen said, there was a time when heaven, earth, and sea did not exist. In all the universe there was nothing but a region of boiling flame and a region of cold with a great gap lying between. Rivers of ice pushed out into this gap, and the red heat of the fires from the other side beat fiercely upon them. Steam arose, and the whole space was filled with swirling mist.

At last these clouds took shape, and out of them Ymer, the first frost giant, was born. Next, the shifting particles formed a great cow, by whose milk Ymer was nourished. Thereupon he grew greatly in vigor, and his vague outline became clear and firm. In this way the frost giant was given life, and in time sons and daughters were born to him out of the mist.

In the meantime the cow who had nurtured the frost giant found no nourishment herself. Eventually she began to lick at the ice blocks which were pushed out of the region of cold. As the ice melted under her rough tongue, it shaped itself into the outline of a huge head. The cow licked further, and features became distinct. She licked again, and blue eyes opened. At last this other huge creature was formed, and he rose up and looked at the misty gap in which the vast shapes of the frost giants could be vaguely seen.

This being was Bure, who was ancestor of the gods, and great power was in him. The moment he beheld the frost giants, he knew they were evil and resolved to destroy them. He cried aloud upon his son and his grandsons who were yet unborn, until the whole gap thundered and rolled with the echoes of his mighty voice. Out of his warm breath and the power of his magic, his descendants were born. Then the gods lifted up their arms and rushed against the frost giants. The mists of the gap swirled in confusion as the two races battled in their midst.

Bure was slain in the mighty struggle, but the gods destroyed Ymer at last and routed their enemies. The remaining frost giants fled into the outer regions of the great gap, where they made themselves a land of mountains and mist to dwell in.

As the thunder of combat died away, Bure's grandson, Allfather Odin, looked down on Ymer's vast body which sprawled across the center of the gap. "The frost giant was made out of mist," said he, "and his form is still fluid. Let us shape it anew into a world for us all to dwell in."

The other gods gladly agreed. "Ymer's body shall be earth," they declared, and they formed it into land, round and flat like a wheel. In the center they piled mountains, for there they planned to build Asgard, which was to be their home and strong citadel. Next they took Ymer's misty skull for the great arch of heaven. They changed his blood into blue ocean water, which they poured around the outer edge of the earth as a barrier between themselves and Giantland. They stole sparks from the fiery regions to light the stars, and built chariots in which they set sun and moon spirits to ride over the earth.

In this way the world was created, but though Ymer was dead, his body was divine, and life of a kind was still in it. Grass began to grow on the earth. Forests sprang up and animals appeared. "We must make rulers for these things," said Odin at last. "Let us shape beings like ourselves who shall watch over the earth and make it prosper."

Under the ground and on the earth's surface small, creeping things had come to life. The gods made these like themselves, and in this way the light elves and dark dwarfs were born. Neither race pleased the gods entirely. The dwarfs were wonderful craftsmen, but their nature was evil, and they fled into the caverns of the earth to live in darkness out of sight of the gods. The elves blessed the animals and crops, but they built their own home of Elfland up in the air.

"These races are not truly our creation," said Odin. "They had life of themselves, and we only gave them shape. Let us make a new master on earth." This time the gods took trees from the forest, breathed life into them, and formed them into Woman and Man.

Men and women looked to the gods for protection, but the power of the gods was limited. Many things appeared in the world which were not created by the gods and opposed them. Beyond earth there still dwelt the frost giants. Hel, the monstrous daughter of a god and a giantess, built a kingdom of darkness under the earth, where she ruled over the spirits of the dead. The great world serpent encircled the earth at the bottom of the sea. Dark wolves pursued the chariots of the terrified sun and moon. Far above the earth, demons were born in the regions of boiling fire. All these great forces of evil threatened the world, and none knew whether they or the gods would prevail.

Odin was the master of the gods, and he was infinitely wise, for he had paid with the sight of one keen, blue eye for a drink from the waters of wisdom. It now seemed to him time to talk to the maidens in whose hands the future lay. These were the Norns, or Fates, some of whom were said to be elves, some dwarfs. In any case, they lived in the heavens near the upper end of the rainbow, which was the bridge between sky and earth.

The Norns sat by a many-colored fountain whose spray rose behind them like a rainbow in the air. The veils before their faces were thick and mysterious as clouds stirring and twisting in the wind. It seemed as though these would blow aside and reveal the face of the future, yet behind each fold lay always another, for none could pierce the mystery of the Norns.

"Greeting to you, Odin, Allfather," said the eldest slowly. "Greeting, Creator of the earth, and Ruler until the Day of Doom."

Odin leaned on his spear and stood watching, while wind blew out his sky-blue mantle and fluttered his white cloud of hair. "Tell me of the Day of Doom," he said at last. "How long shall my rule endure?"

The hand of the Norn was yellow and old. She raised it to draw her veil closer. "Ages of human lives," was all she said.

"How shall I fall?"

"In battle."

"Tell me what shall happen on that day."

"All evil shall assemble against you," answered the slow, deep voice of the Norn. "The serpent shall arise from the ocean with poison dripping from his jaws. The wolves of evil and darkness will come ravening to the fray. Heimdall, your watchman, shall trumpet his warning as fire demons pour down from above across the rainbow bridge. The giants will wade the ocean to battle. Hel shall arise from the land of the dead."

"Who will fight on my side?" demanded Odin.

"The spirits of the mighty dead," said she. "You will choose Valkyries, warrior maidens, and mount them on horses of cloud to ride over the battlefields of men. They will snatch up the souls of dying heroes and carry them to Valhalla, your lofty, shield-roofed hall. There they shall feast and practice their weapons, for they are to be your army in the battles of the Day of Doom."

"If I must perish on that day," said Allfather Odin, "tell me at least what shall endure."

"Nothing that now exists," said the aged Norn. "Thor, your mighty son, shall be slain by the serpent. Bright Frey will be destroyed by the fire spirits. Earth shall be burned to ashes. Wolves shall swallow the sun and moon."

"All then will be lost."

"No, not all," she answered. "Sons of your sons shall survive, and though you fall, the giants and the demons shall be utterly destroyed. Then the new race of gods will make a new, pure heaven and earth, from which all evil will have passed away."

The old Norn lifted her hand once more to her veil. Through it Odin gazed deep into sunken eyes blue and piercing as his own. "That is good," he said slowly. "I was made for battle, and mine will be the age of the fighter. Let other gods rule when the struggle is over. I will ride the howling tempest and perish in the last great storm."

The Norn turned away with a slow movement, but Odin looked long at her, her companions, and the shifting colors of the water behind. "Asgard, our citadel, is on earth," he said at last. "Here, near the wise ones, our judgment seat shall be. We will set Heimdall, our watchman, to guard the rainbow bridge, over which we will mount daily to heaven and give laws for the ruling of the world."

The Creation

1. Compare this creation myth with that of the Greeks. How is it different? How is it the same?
2. Out of the swirling mists that arose when the regions of cold and heat met, the frost kings were formed. Later, Bure, the ancestor of the gods, was uncovered. Whom do you think these beings symbolize?
3. Man, created by the gods, looked to them for protection. But the primitive people who created these stories were well aware that there were forces of evil as well as of good in their lives. The Greeks blamed much evil on the fickleness of the gods. How did the Norsemen explain it?
4. In Greek mythology it was Prometheus who could foretell the future. And of course the oracles could also see forthcoming events. Who could see into the future in the Norse myths? Why do you think the end of the world is foretold in the beginning?
5. Compare Zeus and Odin. What differences are apparent? What do these differences tell you about the people who created the two rulers?

Do you remember the monstrous brood of youngsters that Uranus imprisoned? Loki, the fire god, also had some fearful children. One of them, a giant wolf whose vast jaws stretched from earth to heaven, was a cause of concern to all the gods. Here you will find out how they temporarily brought him under control.

The Fenris Wolf

Olivia E. Coolidge

Though Loki, the fire god, was handsome and ready-witted, his nature was really evil. He was, indeed, the cause of most of the misfortunes which befell the gods. He was constantly in trouble, yet often forgiven because the gods valued his cleverness. It was he who found ways out of difficulty for them, so that for a long time they felt that they could not do without him.

In the early days Loki, though a god, had wedded a monstrous giantess, and the union of these two evil beings produced a fearful brood. The first was the great world serpent, whom Odin cast into the sea, and

who became so large that he completely encircled the earth, his tail touching his mouth. The second was Hel, the grisly goddess of the underworld, who reigned in the horrible land of the dead. The third was the most dreadful of all, a huge monster called the Fenris Wolf.

When the gods first saw the Fenris Wolf, he was so young that they thought they could tame him. They took him to Asgard, therefore, and brave Tyr undertook to feed and train him. Presently, however, the black monster grew so enormous that his open jaws would stretch from heaven to earth, showing teeth as large as the trunks of oak trees and as sharply pointed as knives. The howls of the beast were so dreadful as he tore his vast meals of raw meat that the gods, save for Tyr, dared not go near him, lest he devour them.

At last all were agreed that the Fenris Wolf must be fettered if they were to save their very lives, for the monster grew more ferocious towards them every day. They forged a huge chain, but since none was strong enough to bind him, they challenged him to a trial of strength. "Let us tie you with this to see if you can snap the links," said they.

The Fenris Wolf took a look at the chain and showed all his huge white teeth in a dreadful grin. "Bind me if you wish," he growled, and he actually shut his eyes as he lay down at ease to let them put it on.

The Fenris Wolf

The gods stepped back, and the wolf gave a little shake. There was a loud cracking sound, and the heavy links lay scattered around him in pieces. The wolf howled in triumph until the sun and moon in heaven trembled at the noise.

Thor, the smith, called other gods to his aid, and they labored day and night at a second chain. This was half as strong again as the first, and so heavy that no one of the gods could drag it across the ground. "This is by far the largest chain that was ever made," said they. "Even the Fenris Wolf will not be able to snap fetters such as these."

Once more they brought the chain to the wolf, and he let them put it on, though this time it was clear that he somewhat doubted his strength. When they had chained him, he shook himself violently, but the fetters held. His great, red eyes burned with fury, the black hair bristled on his back, and he gnashed his teeth until the foam flew. He strained heavily against the iron until the vast links flattened and lengthened, but did not break. Finally with a great bound and a howl he dashed himself against the ground, and suddenly the chain sprang apart so violently that broken pieces were hurled about the heads of the watching gods.

Now the gods realized in despair that all their strength and skill would not avail to bind the wolf. Therefore Odin sent a messenger to the dwarf people under the earth, bidding them forge him a chain. The messenger returned with a little rope, smooth and soft as a silken string, which was hammered on dwarfish anvils out of strange materials which have never been seen or heard. The sound of a cat's footfall, the breath of a fish, the flowing beard of a woman, and the roots of a mountain made the metal from which it was forged.

The gods took the little rope to the Fenris Wolf. "See what an easy task we have for you this time," they said. "Why should I bother myself with a silken string?" asked the wolf sullenly. "I have broken your mightiest chain. What use is this foolish thing?"

"The rope is stronger than it looks," answered they. "We are not able to break it, but it will be a small matter to you."

"If this rope is strong by enchantment," said the wolf in slow suspicion, "how can I tell that you will loosen me if I cannot snap it after all? On one condition you may bind me: you must give me a hostage from among yourselves."

"How can we do this?" they asked.

The Fenris Wolf stretched himself and yawned until the sun hid behind clouds at the sight of his great, red throat. "I will let you bind me with this rope," he said, "if one of you gods will hold his hand between my teeth while I do it."

The gods looked at one another in silence. The wolf grinned from ear to ear. Without a word Tyr walked forward and laid his bare hand inside the open mouth.

The gods bound the great wolf, and he stretched himself and heaved as before. This time, however, he did not break his bonds. He gnashed his jaws together, and Tyr cried out in pain as he lost his hand. Nevertheless, the great black wolf lay howling and writhing and helplessly biting the ground. There he lay in the bonds of the silken rope as long as the reign of Odin endured. The Fates declared, however, that in the last days, when the demons of ice and fire should come marching against the gods to the battlefield, the great sea would give up the serpent, and the Fenris Wolf would break his bonds. The wolf would swallow Odin, and the gods would go down in defeat. Sun and moon would be devoured, and the whole earth would perish utterly.

QUESTIONS FOR DISCUSSION

1. In what way could Loki be considered the father of evil? What was the relationship of his offspring to the universe?
2. What is the subject of this myth? Is the subject two-fold? Explain.
3. Who is the hero of the story? According to Norse mythology, a hero is one who resists evil even though he faces defeat. How does Tyr fit this definition? What actions and words does the author choose in order to make us see that Tyr is a hero?
4. In an earlier myth the Norns indicated what would occur in the "last days." Read the last three lines of the story. Why was Odin's victory only a partial one? Which triumphed in the end, good or evil?

Understanding Words

Words That Cause Confusion

Sometimes words that are similar in spelling or pronunciation cause confusion. In the second paragraph, we are introduced to Hel, the *grisly* goddess of the underworld. You have perhaps at some time heard a man's beard referred to as being *grizzly*. The two words sound the same, but they certainly do not mean the same thing. *Grisly* means "horrible, gruesome, or ghastly." *Grizzly* means "streaked with gray."

Write sentences to show you understand the meanings of the following words that are often confused.

accept-except   adapt-adopt   affect-effect
allusion-illusion   its-it's   principal-principle

Can you think of other similar words that are often confused?

SUGGESTED ACTIVITIES

1. Prepare a sheet of paper for the writing of two lists. Head the first list "Exaggerations" and the second, "Imagery — Color and Motion." Read the story of "The Fenris Wolf" again and find words that will fit into these lists.
2. The story follows the three-part arrangement of a short story — beginning, middle, and end. Write sentences summarizing each of the three parts. Consider whether the last three sentences in the story should have been omitted.
3. Words or phrases such as "Thor the smith" or "Loki the fire god" are used to describe characteristics of a person or a thing. These expressions are called *epithets*. Can you make up some epithets to describe persons or things around school?
4. How would you personify evil? That is, what human characteristics would you attribute to evil? Write a short paragraph describing your newly created being. Seek to use verbs which will help your reader or listener to picture your creation.

The Norse gods did not have to worry about building permits, but when they decided to build a great banquet hall down by the sea, they ran into trouble all the same. Aegir, the sea god, was appalled at the thought of noisy gods for neighbors. And thus the adventure begins. . . .

Hymer's Caldron

Olivia E. Coolidge

Aegir, the sea god, lay on the rocks of a headland with a blanket of cloud pulled about him and his old eyes peacefully closed. He was smiling gently to himself while he listened to the laughter of his grey daughters, the waves, as they ran up the sloping beach. Into his musing broke the loud voices of the gods, who came clamoring for permission to build a banqueting hall by the ocean where the green hills ran down to the sea.

Old Aegir rent the mist and rose up, long and dank. "You have reared your citadel of Asgard in the center of the earth," grumbled he. "Why do you not use that for your feasting? Have you not great halls there roofed with silver and shining with gold?"

"The earth is ours," said Allfather Odin. "We build where we choose, yet since this disturbs you, ask us for some gift in return. We will buy your good will."

The sea god smiled cunningly. "You will need to brew mead for great feasts," he said. "Bring me, therefore, before you build, a caldron a full mile wide and a full mile deep." Then Aegir sank down on the rocks, and mist enfolded him once more.

The gods returned wondering to Asgard, for such a great caldron had never been seen on earth. "In the hall of the frost giant, Hymer, hangs such a caldron," said brave Tyr at last. "This earth is ours, but Giantland across the great ocean is wilder and yet unconquered. Who dares go thither with me?"

"I will come," answered red-bearded Thor. "Make ready my chariot."

Tyr put on a coat of mail, but Thor went in his blue tunic with his red arms bare to the elbow. He took no weapon but his hammer, which was so heavy that ten could not lift it, though Thor swung it with ease.

Hymer's Caldron

Red-eyed goats, shaggy and fierce as their master, drew his chariot. Their iron hoofs echoed on rocks and rumbled on turf as they carried him thundering over the mountains to the dark ocean, which was the boundary of the earth. On the other side of this lay Giantland, a country of frozen hills and dark valleys too deep to behold the sun. Far over the heads of the gods stretched endless mountains clothed with pine. Black waters thundered beneath the ice. Great rocks roared down the mountain sides. Wolves howled and echoes answered. Enormous footprints showed in the snowy waste.

So huge was the hall of Hymer that the roof of it went up to the sky. Clouds sailed in and out through the smoke vents, making a ceiling far under its massive beams. So wide were the stone pillars that the two gods themselves could not have joined hands around one of them. A vast fire in the middle of the hall was consuming twenty whole trees, branches and all.

Hymer's wife was fair as the snow and gold as the winter sun. Her eyes were like a blue, cold sky, but they smiled on the gods. "Welcome, lords of the earth," she said as she brought them long drinking horns of ale. "Hymer goes fishing daily for the mighty monsters of the deep. He will be angry at your coming, yet since you have drunk as his guests, he will keep the peace. Only stand behind a pillar when he enters, lest the deadly glance of his anger destroy you instantly."

Presently they heard that the giant was coming, for the ground shook beneath his tread. Thor and Tyr moved behind a pillar as the iron-studded door swung wide. The white frost giant stood on the threshold with snow flying about him and the long icicles clattering in his bushy beard.

"Who came this way?" he shouted, while his frosty glare ranged round the hall and came to rest on the pillar behind which the two gods stood. So fierce was his icy gaze that the pillar froze and cracked apart. It fell to the ground with a thunderous crash, and the two gods stood revealed.

"You are not welcome, strangers from Asgard," said the giant sullenly, "but I see you have drunk my ale. Stay therefore in peace this once, but do not dare to cross my path again."

Thor lifted his mighty hammer. His beard jutted out, and his fierce, blue eyes were aflame. Quickly Tyr said, "We will feast with you tonight, O frost giant, and tomorrow we will go in peace. Woe to you, however, if you venture on earth where we reign."

"So be it," answered the giant sulkily as he flung himself down in his carved seat.

Three oxen had been killed in the courtyard, skinned, and cut up for their meal. The huge pieces were thrown into a great pot which sat sizzling on the fire. Vast though this was, other ones yet larger hung on hooks from the pillars. Thor saw that the greatest one was indeed a mile wide and a full mile deep, as the old sea god had described it.

The giant speared the side of an ox from the boiling stew and began his meal without another word. Thor arose and seized two sides to eat likewise. Each time the giant took a joint, Thor took two until the pot was empty. The giant looked up in wrath. "You eat me out of cattle," he roared. "Never was there such a guest."

"Giant," cried Thor eagerly, for an idea had come into his head, "I will fish with you tomorrow in return for this meal, and whatever I catch shall be yours."

"Your little arms will haul in no great catch," grumbled the giant, but his anger was softened somewhat, and he left his guests in peace.

Next morning, when the giant was making ready his gear, Thor asked his host for bait and hook. "Find them yourself," said the giant sullenly.

Without a word, Thor seized a mighty hook and went out to the pasture. He killed a great black ox, the largest there, and came down with its head to the boat. The giant looked at it and opened his lips to speak, for

Hymer's Caldron

it was the best of his cattle. But Thor merely turned away and took the oars. "I will row you out," he said.

"You will not row far," said the giant. He settled his great bulk in the bow and sat there in silence, though the boat shot through the water with amazing speed. Presently he said, "Here is the place," and bent forward to bait his hook.

"I fish farther from land," answered Thor calmly and rowed on till the hills of Giantland lay like a distant cloud on the edge of the sea. Here he stopped.

"Turn back," protested the giant. "Beneath us in the middle of the ocean the great world serpent lies. His head and his tail meet together, while his body encircles the earth."

"I dare fish here," answered Thor, stooping to bait his hook. "Sit still and watch if you do not. All giants are cowards at heart."

The giant cast out his hook at that, and two whales leaped upon it. The iron went through both of them, and the sea boiled as they lashed and tried to dive. The giant braced his feet on the bottom of the boat while he pulled the huge fish slowly in.

Thor tied a great lump of lead to his baited hook and cast it into the sea. Down it went into the green depths, but the monsters who live there let it go, for it was too big for them. Still further down into the black waters it sunk, far below the light of the sun, where red and blue fish glowed in the pitchy dark. Then the great world serpent lifted his head from the slime and snatched at it. As the hook bit into him, he shuddered throughout his length until great waves arose on the surface of the sea and lashed the distant coasts.

Thor stood up with his feet apart, teeth clenched, and his broad face red with strain. The boat danced like a feather on the boiling waters. Thor heaved, while the frightened giant clung helpless to the gunwales, dumb with fear of the black water, in which he would sink like lead. Thor panted. The boat whirled like a stone on a string. Yard by yard the line grew shorter. At length right by the gunwale the livid head of the serpent rose to the surface of the water. Its red eyes, a foot across, blinked at its captor. The poison dripping from its vast jaws hissed and bubbled in the waves. Its flickering fangs struck madly at the boat.

Thor gathered the line in one hand and smote at the beast with the other, turning his face aside from the poisonous spray. The creature moaned and shuddered. Far beneath the sea the foundations of the world were shaken. Earth quivered. Clefts opened in the mountains, and burning lava streamed forth onto the fields. Thor raised his arm again. The black fangs stabbed once more from the bleeding mouth. The gunwale dipped to the very edge of the poisoned foam. With a sudden spring the giant leaped forward and cut the line.

The boat rocked back. Thor staggered and fell headlong. The wounded monster sank hissing into the deep. At last the boiling waves subsided, and the rocking earth stood still. The giant took up his oars and rowed desperately for home, while Thor sat panting in the half-filled boat, glaring at his companion. Neither spoke till the keel grounded on the beach of Giantland.

"Pull up the boat or carry the fish," grumbled the giant. "Must I do all the work?"

"Give me the boat," said Thor. He lifted it up on his back with water and whales and all. He threw it down in the courtyard with a crash. "You spoiled my catch," he said.

"Take a present in return, but go," said the giant.

"Give me your mile-wide caldron," answered the god.

"Now that is too much," said the giant. "I meant some smaller thing. You pulled a heavy line, but you did not strike much of a blow. Take this drinking cup and shatter it. If you can, I will give you the caldron."

Thor raised the cup and hurled it against one of the pillars of stone. Great chips flew from the pillar, but the cup fell unharmed to the ground. The frost giant laughed, but his wife came to the gods bearing each a brimming horn. "Strike on the head of the frost giant," she said softly. "His skull is harder than rock."

Hymer's Caldron

Thor leaped for the cup and hurled it at the giant's frozen head. It landed full on his forehead and shivered to pieces. The giant looked at them a moment. "Well, take the caldron," he said. He smiled as he spoke, for Tyr leaped up and tugged at the caldron, but he could not lift it an inch to slide it off its hook. "Take the caldron, brave god," said the giant again, and he laughed at the struggling Tyr.

Thor put him aside and slid the caldron down from its hook. He seized it by the rim, lifted it high, and settled it upside down on his shoulders. He groped for the door, his head in the pot and the long handles hitting his heels. He stumbled over the threshold with Tyr as his guide. Together they reeled across the valley and down to the shore. The giant burst out into laughter to see them go, and the roaring echoes answered him back from every side.

Thus Thor won the caldron, and the gods built themselves a banqueting hall roofed with silver and lighted with burning gold. They had no servants, for the mead and the ale bore themselves to the shining horns. Odin sat in the high seat, and by him were Frey and his father, old Njord, brave Tyr, Hermod, and Heimdall, and Loki, the father of wrong. But Thor had gone out once more for adventure and stood again on the coasts of Giantland, shaking his hammer at monsters, and giants, and the shadowy wolf that ran through the heavens in pursuit of the fleeing sun. One later time he wrestled with the world serpent, but the giant king had enchanted his eyes, so that he did not know what monster it was with whom he strove. At last on the Day of Doom he was fated to slay his enemy, but to perish himself in its poisoned jaws.

QUESTIONS FOR DISCUSSION

1. The Greek gods reminded us of people. Do these hardy Norse gods also seem very human? Explain.
2. Do you recognize the narrative pattern in this myth? Construct a diagram of it.
3. What characteristics did Thor possess that helped him meet the test and win the caldron?
4. The ending of this story is humorous. Try to think of a proverb that could explain it in a few words?
5. How is suspense created in the story? What reasons can you give for the inclusion of the last few sentences after the conclusion of the story? Has this information been included in other myths you have read thus far?
6. What would you say are the teller's feelings about Thor? Does he like him? Or does he think he is a bit too proud? Support your ideas with concrete examples from the story.

SUGGESTED ACTIVITIES

1. There are many conflicts between gods and giants and good and evil in the Norse myths. Write a paragraph stating reasons for these conflicts. Try to decide whether they could have been solved without fights and battles.
2. A statement that goes beyond the truth is called an exaggeration. How heavy was Thor's hammer? How large was Hymer's house? How wide were the stone pillars? Find other examples of exaggeration. Why does the author use exaggerations? How do these statements make you feel?
3. To help you see and feel the danger in the boat, the teller uses particular phrases to create pictures in your mind or to appeal to your senses; for example, "he would sink like lead," and "the boat whirled like a stone on a string." In these descriptions the author has used a figure of speech called a *simile*, which makes an imaginative comparison by the use of the word *like*. In other similes the comparison is expressed by the use of *as, than, similar to,* or *resembles.* Discuss other similes found in the story.
4. Color words such as "the red-eyed goats," "blue cold sky," "red and blue fish," and "white frost giant" appeal to the sense of sight. What is the effect created by the use of these words in the story? What do you think was the author's reason for using them? •

Hymer's Caldron

Here is another adventure of Thor and Loki, and it's as lively as the last. If you have ever exaggerated your good points (just a little), then you will sympathize with poor Thor.

Thor and the Giant King

Olivia E. Coolidge

Thor and Loki in a goat-drawn chariot rumbled through the air faster than wind. As night was falling, they neared the great sea which surrounds the earth. "I see a small farmhouse," said Loki, peering through the dusk. "Let us go there for shelter."

"We will descend to the earth," answered Thor, "lest we frighten the peasants here."

The great forms of the gods shrank to mortal size, and the goats trotted over the pasture with their chariot bumping behind.

Pine torches were already lit in the peasant's rude cottage. He himself was by the fireside whittling a plow handle. The son of the house was out feeding the oxen, but the peasant's wife sat sewing, while the daughter stirred a porridge of water and meal, which was all the supper they had.

"Welcome, strangers!" cried the master of the house. "You are in time to share our supper, poor though it is. Beds we have none, but Thjalfe, my son, shall fetch you an armful of dry, fresh rushes. Wife, bring our guests some ale."

The old woman offered thin beer in rude, wooden cups. Thor and Loki sat down on the bench beside the fire. Presently above the smells of damp clothes and wood smoke which pervaded the air, Thor's nose detected the scent of the porridge which the daughter still stirred in the iron pot. His face went blank with disgust. "Is this all you have to set before us?" he inquired.

"We are no lords that we should eat meat every day," answered the peasant.

"Thjalfe," cried Thor, turning to the son, who had just come in, "take my two goats and kill them for supper. Only before you put them in the pot, bring me their skins."

Thjalfe hastened to do his bidding, and presently the whole family was seated around an appetizing meal. First, however, Thor spread the goatskins in a corner. "Cast all the bones in these skins," he commanded, "and be careful to break none." He did not notice that Thjalfe had broken a thigh bone before he threw it in the corner with the rest.

The next morning Thor tapped the bones of his goats with his hammer and made them arise again younger and stronger than ever, save that one was now lame. When Thor beheld this and knew that he had been disobeyed, he was terribly angry. His great red eyebrows came down over his eyes, and he gripped his huge hammer with such force that his knuckles turned white. The unfortunate peasant and his family sank to their knees imploring his mercy.

"Spare at least my parents," pleaded Thjalfe, "for they are not at fault. As for me, I will go with you to be your servant if you will but grant me my life."

Thor's frown relaxed, and he nodded, appeased. "That is good," said he. "Thjalfe shall become my servant, and I will leave my goats here in his father's care until the broken leg is healed." Thus the two gods and their new servant set out on foot, Thjalfe carrying a bag of provisions. Across the great sea they traveled, to Giantland, a trackless country of great forests and barren heaths, where they wandered for a long time without seeing giant or dwelling.

At last as dark approached, they came to a strange hall with no doors or windows, but a great, irregular opening at one end. Inside, it was dark and empty, but since the wind blew chill, the three travelers were glad enough to sleep there on the floor.

*Thor and
the Giant King*

87

They were awakened in the middle of the night by a terrible noise and an earthquake. Loki and Thjalfe felt their way into one of a row of small inner chambers which opened from the hall, and lay there huddled together, trying not to listen to the dreadful sounds. Thor took his hammer in his hands and sat in the great hall until daylight, when he crawled out to find the source of the fearsome roaring.

A man the size of a mountain was lying snoring across their path. The earth shook as his chest rose and fell. He was so huge that as he lay, Thor could only just reach up to shout in his ear.

"Hey! Hallo! What's that? What squeaked?" said the giant, sitting up and rubbing his eyes. "Well, little fellow, what do you want? Hey! Get out of my glove!" He picked up the strange-looking hall in which they had spent the night and fitted it on his hand.

"We are traveling in Giantland," shouted Thor. "We come in peace."

"Oho! Doubtless King Utgard-Loke will be glad to hear that," laughed the giant. "You think a good deal of yourself, I see, but I warn you that at the king's court, I am not particularly large. Unless I am much mistaken, you will not be greatly regarded there."

"Where is the king's court?" asked Thor.

"To the North. I am going that way, but I am in no hurry. If you start out over the hill, I will overtake you and put you on the road."

Thjalfe shouldered his sack in haste, and the three companions set out as fast as their legs would carry them. The giant ate, slept, and waited until noon. Then in three strides he was up with the gods, who were toiling, hungry and thirsty, over a dusty plain. "I see I must carry your sack," said he good-naturedly. "Let me put it in mine. I will give it back this evening when the time comes to make a meal." He scooped up the sack of provisions from Thjalfe and was out of sight in three strides.

Thor looked grimly at his companions. "If we are to eat, we must catch up with this giant," said he. The three hastened over the hills until sunset. When it was almost dark, they made out the huge form in the distance and quickened their flagging steps.

"Here you are at last!" cried the giant. "I thought you were never coming. Take my sack and open it, for I have eaten and am ready for sleep." He tossed over his sack and lay down. Presently the whole place resounded with snores.

"I cannot open this sack," said Thjalfe.

"Let Thor try," said Loki wearily. "He is the strongest, and I am too hungry to wait any more."

Thor took the sack and tugged at the strings, but try as he would, he could neither loosen or break them. "Wake up!" he yelled to the giant, but his voice was drowned in the noise of snoring.

The three companions looked at one another in despair. "Wait a moment," said Thor between his teeth. "I have something with me that can make even giants pay attention." He took out his hammer and strode up to the monstrous head. Drawing himself up to his full height, he whirled his weapon and brought it down on the giant's forehead with the full strength of both arms.

"Ugh!" said the giant thickly. He put up a hand and turned over. "What tickled?" he asked sleepily. "Did a leaf fall out of the tree?"

Thor put up his hammer completely crestfallen. "We shall have to eat in the morning," said he to his companions with as much authority as he could muster. "You had better go to sleep."

"I am far too hungry," grumbled Loki. "Besides, he makes such an earthshaking noise!"

All three lay down, but while the snoring went on, sleep was impossible. The more Thor thought of his blow, the more certain he felt that he must have missed the giant altogether in the darkness. "Unlikely though that may seem," he said to himself, "it is less incredible than that he should not have felt Mjolnir, the mightiest weapon on earth."

Presently his fury at hunger and sleeplessness got the better of him, and he crept out to try again. He took care this time to find his way to a rock where he stood right over the giant and could feel his beard fluttering in the fierce wind of the monster's breath. He whirled the hammer three times, brought it down, and felt it sink into something yielding.

"What is the matter with this tree?" said the giant sitting up crossly. "There must be birds in it. They are throwing down twigs in my face." He lay down once more.

"I cannot believe it," said Thor grimly to himself. "I felt my hammer sink in. I must try again when it is light."

The grey light of morning dawned at last on a miserable trio, cold, sleepless, and hungry, regarding the giant with furious eyes. "Just let him wait until I can see him," said Thor at intervals all night long. "He will notice Mjolnir this time, I can promise."

By the faint light the giant's face, though indistinct, was clear enough. With a terrible blow Thor buried his hammer, head and handle, deep in the mighty forehead.

"Agh!" said the giant this time. "Those birds!" he complained. "I hope you slept out in the open. They keep throwing down moss in my face." He looked around. "Why, you are awake and ready to go. You are in a great hurry, though I fear King Utgard-Loke will not think you very important. Still, his citadel lies but a short distance ahead. My way now takes me elsewhere." With that he got up, lifted his sack, and was gone in three strides.

"There goes our breakfast," said Loki. "I hope Utgard-Loke is near!"

It was not long until they saw the giant king's citadel, but it was many hours before they came close to it. It towered so huge in front of

them that, though they craned their necks, they could not see the top of the wall. The great, locked gate had bars the thickness of oak trees, but the spaces between them were so wide that the gods could easily creep through.

King Utgard-Loke sat in his hall amid a company of mountainous giants. "Who are you, little fellows?" asked he, looking down on the gods.

"I am Thor," answered the god, "and these are Loki and my servant. We have traveled hither to visit the king of Giantland."

"You are welcome, little gods," said the king. "I had not expected that you would be so small. Nevertheless, if you are indeed Thor and Loki, you should be able to show us some feats, for it is our custom to prove our guests before we sit down to the feast. Tell us, therefore, what you will do."

"I," said Loki immediately, "will eat more and faster than anyone in your company."

"That is a fine wager," said the king laughingly. "Loge here is considered a fast eater among us, but no doubt he is outclassed by you. We will put a trough of meat between you and let one start at each end. We shall soon see who is the better.

Loki was ravenous with hunger. Even Thor marveled at his appetite. Yet fast as he ate, Loge did equally well. When the two met finally in the middle of the trough, Loki had eaten all the meat, but Loge had eaten meat, bones, and the trough itself. He was therefore adjudged the winner. "Never mind," whispered Loki to Thor. "At least I have had my fill!"

The Bayeux Tapestry

"Loki is not very impressive," remarked the giant king. "What now will you show us?"

"I will run a race with anyone you care to put forward," cried Thjalfe, who was the swiftest of mankind.

"Come with us, Huge," said the giant king. "Let us go out to the race course."

Huge and Thjalfe were set to race, and though Thjalfe ran like the wind, Huge touched the goal and turned to face his rival before Thjalfe could come up with him. The second time they ran, there was a long bolt shot between them. The third time, Huge turned back from the winning post to meet Thjalfe still only halfway along the course.

"I do not think Thjalfe has brought you much credit," said the king, "but now that we come to Thor himself, the tale is bound to be different. Tell us, great Thor, what will you do?"

Thor was angered at the mockery of the king's tone, and he was still somewhat cast down by his failure of the night before. Therefore he refrained from trials of strength and said sulkily, "I am called a deep drinker. Perhaps I can astonish you with that."

"Bring here my horn," cried the king. "My young men empty this at a draught. A poor drinker takes two, but I have never yet known one who could not empty it in three."

The horn seemed very long to Thor, but it was not wide. He put his lips down to the brim, lest he spill it, but as he drank more deeply, he tried to tilt it to his mouth. To his surprise, the horn would not move, and he was forced to bend over it. At last he straightened up exhausted and saw in astonishment that it was almost impossible to tell whether it were emptier than before.

"That is not much of a draught," said the king, "but perhaps you are saving your strength for your second one."

Thor bent down angrily, but the second time that he stopped for breath, he had only emptied the horn enough for it to be carried without spilling.

"I do not think your feats are as great as your reputation," remarked the king. "You have left a great deal for your last draught."

Thor bent down again and drank with all his might, but though this was the mightiest draught he had ever taken, he could not empty the horn. Its contents were visibly less, but that was all. He pushed it away sullenly. "Let me try something else," said he.

"I have heard much of your strength," answered the king, "and I would gladly see something of it, yet I dare not set you a hard task, since I perceive you are not such a hero as I had thought. Will you try to lift my cat from the floor?"

A huge, grey cat sprang forward. Thor put his shoulders under its middle, but the cat only arched its back, and he could not lift it an inch. At last he got both hands under one paw, and by tugging and straining managed to raise it a little.

"Let be," said the king. "Every child among us could do that feat."

"I will wrestle with anyone and beat him," cried Thor, "for now my blood is up."

"I do not think I can ask my young men to wrestle with you," answered the king. "It seems hardly worth their while. Nevertheless you may try a fall with my old nurse, Elle, if you wish."

Thor advanced upon the old woman in anger, but though he put forth all his strength, he could not budge her. After a while she in her turn tightened her grasp. Thor's footing failed him, and after hard struggles he was forced down on one knee.

"That is enough," said the king. "It is not worth contesting with you. Sit down and take your supper, but in future let other people boast."

The three companions ate their meal in silence, and early next morning they took their leave. King Utgard-Loke himself went out to say farewell to them and to ask when they were likely to return.

"When I can avenge my disgrace," answered Thor sulkily.

Utgard-Loke laughed. "You are not disgraced, but rather covered with glory," he replied. "If you will promise to visit me no more, I will tell you how that is so."

"I will gladly promise," cried Thor, "if you can convince me of this."

"Know then," said Utgard-Loke, "that I was the giant you met in the forest, and that my size which seemed so great to you, was but an illusion of magic. Do you see those hills over there?"

Thor nodded.

Thor and the Giant King

"That range of hills I brought between my forehead and your hammer as I lay pretending to sleep. See the three great notches you have made in them by blows such as I would have thought incredible, had I not beheld them."

"I knew you must notice Mjolnir," said Thor with a grim laugh.

"For two days I kept you without food and sleep," said the king. "I hoped that you would be discouraged and return to the earth; but if not, at least I might expect that when you came to my court, your strength would be somewhat lessened. Alas, it was not so!"

"I had not thought any of us had shown great prowess," replied Thor.

"You did not think so, but we who beheld you were frightened and amazed. First, Loki had an eating match with Loge, who is fire itself. No wonder Loge burned through bones and trough, and yet Loki ate as much meat as he, after all. As for Thjalfe, he was matched against Huge, who is my thought. It is clear that he had no chance, and yet the first time he ran, he came within an arm's length!"

"What of me, then?"

"The end of the horn that you drank from lay in the sea. When you come to the shore, you will see how greatly the water was ebbed. We all held our breath for a moment and thought that, though it was clearly impossible, you might actually drink the ocean dry. The cat in turn was none other than the serpent who lies stretched around the sea, his tail meeting his mouth. When you raised the monster's back to the sky, you appeared about to tear it from its resting place. When you actually lifted it a little, we feared lest the Day of Doom was upon us!"

"I have fought with the serpent before," said Thor. "I wish I had known the creature again, for this time it would not have escaped me."

"Last of all, you wrestled with Elle, who is Old Age. None may ever get the better of her!"

"I see you have thoroughly fooled us," said Thor, "but it is now my turn." With that he lifted his hammer, but the great form of the giant dissolved into wavering mist before his eyes. A mocking laugh sounded near him. Thor whirled in fury and beheld the outlines of the citadel and all that it contained grow dim. In another second they too had scattered into air.

"Remember your promise," said the voice. "Never again!"

"I suppose not," answered Thor glumly. "Nevertheless, should I meet you some time by chance, beware!"

"I will not leave that to chance," answered the voice. "Farewell."

Thor shouldered his weapon and set out with his companions across the long, dusty plains to the sea.

QUESTIONS FOR DISCUSSION

1. What do you learn about the life, customs, and beliefs of the Norse peasants? What do you learn about the gods?
2. In describing the contest between Loki and fire, the author talks about fire as if it were a person. This figure of speech is called *personification;* it gives to inanimate, or non-human, things the form and qualities of human beings. What human qualities were given to the fire? To thought? To old age?
3. What do you think the author is foreshadowing by these words: "Cast all the bones in these skins, and be careful to break none"? What statements foreshadowed the nature of the travelers? The failure of Loki and Thjalfe to meet the test? The continual battle between giants and gods?
4. The author has told this story in a way that revealed the attitudes of the various conflicting forces. What was Thor's outlook on life at the beginning? The peasant's? How did Thor's view change when he assumed the guise of a man? What did Utgard-Loke proclaim when he spoke as the voice at the end?
5. Identify the three parts of this story and show how each builds toward the next.

An Interesting Word

The story tells us that "Pine torches were already lit in the peasant's *rude* cottage." Here *rude* means "crude, rough, or unfinished." Today we more often use it to mean "offensive in manner, discourteous, or uncivilized." The original meaning was simply "natural, raw, or primitive." You will find many words that have shifted their meanings over the years, and it is interesting to see how even in a short time words will take on new meanings. *Nice* once meant "ignorant," and *silly* used to mean "happy." Can you think of more recent examples of words that have changed their meanings?

Recognizing Base Words

"Loki is not very *impressive*," said the Giant King. If you remove the prefix *–im* and the suffix *–ive* you are left with the base word *press*. Many different prefixes and suffixes can be added to this base to form new words. See how many words you can make by combining the following prefixes and suffixes with the base word in a number of different ways.

Prefixes	Suffixes
de-	-or
im-	-ant
com-	-ion
ex-	-ment
re-	-able
sup-	-less
	-ive

Try making new words from the base words *form*, *use*, and *depend*, using some of the prefixes and suffixes given above. Can you think of other base words from which many new words can be made?

SUGGESTION FOR COMPOSITION

Mythology

Invent another adventure of Thor's. Imitate the form of one of the myths and use personification, similes, metaphors, and exaggeration to make your myth interesting. Then read or tell it to the class.

Baldur was "beauty and unclouded joy, pure goodness that knows no evil." All the earth loved him. Of all the gods, he was the brightest, the best. Yet the dread underworld had claimed him. Could he be rescued?

Baldur, the Beautiful

Olivia E. Coolidge

"Arise, great prophetess!" trumpeted a voice in the misty dark. Far over the barren plains rang the loud summons, and the damp, invisible rocks re-echoed, "Arise!"

Nothing stirred in the darkness, and no light showed, save that which gleamed on the spear of the rider and on the flanks of his cloud-grey horse. From the black grave mound before which he stood the muffled voice of the sleeper answered his cry. "Let me rest," it complained. "I have been snowed on, wetted with rain, and drenched with cold dew. I have long been dead. Why rouse me again to feeling?"

"Awake!" cried the rider once more, and he lifted his spear so that the light which shone from it fell on his blue mantle, his dress of grey, and his long, white beard. "I who call you am Odin, Allfather, and I come to learn tidings of Hel."

There was a little movement in the mist on the grave mound, and the voice answered again, nearer now. "I have been long in the kingdom of Hel, grim queen of the dead. What would you learn of that terrible goddess?"

"Why does Hel haunt the dream of Baldur, the radiant one, the most glorious of the gods? Why should she come to him in whose pure presence nothing unclean or ugly has ever till now appeared? What power has Hel over Baldur that she should bring gloom to his brow and dismay to the whole race of gods, whose happiness depends on him?"

"Hel lays claim to bright Baldur," replied the toneless voice of the prophetess. "She bids her servants brew mead for the welcoming feast. She strews her benches with rings and her dais with gold, for she says that Baldur will surely descend to her kingdom, and that she will keep him with her until the Day of Doom."

"Hel must never have Baldur," cried Odin. "Baldur is the treasure of the world. He is beauty and unclouded joy, pure goodness that knows no evil."

"Let me go," moaned the misty shape. "I have answered your question, and to be here in my body is torment. I must return to the dead."

"Sleep again, dread prophetess," said Odin. "Feel no longer the rain and the snow. Hel strews her rings in vain for my son, for we shall know how to keep him from harm."

The mist was still again now, and the grave mound was quiet. Odin set spurs to the great horse, who rose through the air swifter than wind, his mane and tail streaming behind him like grey clouds. The light from the god's spear grew small and vanished in the distance. Silence fell again on the dark land, broken only by the dripping of water from the rocks.

All the gods were saddened by the strange dreams of Baldur and the new look of gloom on his bright face. When, however, Odin brought to Asgard the words of the prophetess, their dismay deepened to black despair. The happiness of Asgard depended upon Baldur, the wisest and most lovely of gods. None could endure the thought of losing him, yet there seemed no way to avoid what the Fates had planned. For a long while there was silence.

"Hel shall not take my son!" cried Odin's wife, Frigga, at last. "I will not endure it! All things on earth shall give me an oath that they will do Baldur no harm."

Frigga hastened out from Asgard, and first she went to the stones and the rocks. All these made oath not to trip her son, Baldur, nor to cut him, nor bruise him, nor hit him. Then she went to the trees and the bushes, who swore not to pierce him, or beat him, or touch him to do any harm. Next she asked the plants which are poisonous, and then the birds and the beasts. Every animal from huge bear to tiny ant promised to spare Baldur, but still the queen of goddesses was not content. She took oaths from the rivers, lest they drown him, from the earth lest it bury him, from fire, snow, and ice, and everything harmful. All things did her bidding gladly for love of the radiant god.

When at last Frigga returned to Asgard, everything had sworn her oath. Even leaves slipped sideways in air, lest they fall upon Baldur. A god, idly flinging a twig near him, saw it check and drop harmless. Intrigued by the sight, he threw a little stone, which glanced aside as though hitting some invisible wall around Baldur. The other gods shouted with glee and tried sticks, stones, spears, and great clubs, none of which would touch him. Some bounced back, some curved in the air, some dropped suddenly right at his feet. Each thing that they threw behaved differently, but none of

them harmed him. One whole summer morning the gods amused themselves watching the many things they flung at the smiling Baldur. Each god thought of something new for his turn, and the crowd laughed loudly at every trick.

Loki, the father of mischief, strolled away from the merry circle. He alone hated Baldur, since his evil nature found no delight in the god who was perfectly pure and good. For a long time he had cunningly hidden his thoughts, so that none suspected that he wished Baldur harm. Loki glanced up at Frigga, who sat smiling down on the sport from the window of her bower. "This is a fine game," he said earnestly, "but is it not dangerous? Surely amid so many things there must be some you have forgotten."

"I went through the whole earth," said Frigga, "and now in my mind I can think of only one thing I have missed. I am certain there are no more."

"But if you have missed one thing," cried Loki, "should not all the gods be warned?"

"Oh, that is only the mistletoe," replied Frigga smiling. "It is such a little shrub that I do not see there is anything it can do."

"I think Baldur must be safe," said Loki walking off with a careless air. "You have indeed relieved my heart."

Loki went out into the forest to search for the mistletoe. It is such a small bush that it was hard for him to find a piece large enough to make a dart. He did so, however, at last, and he sharpened it well. With this in

Baldur, the Beautiful

99

his hand he came back to the courtyard, where the fun was dying down somewhat, though there was still shouting and laughter whenever a new weapon was tried.

Hoder, the brother of Baldur, stood sadly aside from the rest, for he was blind, and all had neglected him, absorbed in their new game. Loki took him by the elbow. "Come, join in the sport," he said.

"How can I?" asked Hoder sadly.

"Come with me and let me guide you." He led Hoder to the circle, planting him straight in front of the smiling Baldur. He put the mistletoe dart in Hoder's hand. "Now strike," he said, "and show them your strength." Hoder, pleased to have entered the game, lunged forward with all his might.

There was a loud cry, and then a terrible silence. The blind god stood puzzled, turning his head from side to side, as though listening for laughter and applause. "Baldur, the beautiful, is dead!" cried someone behind him in a high voice. Still he could not comprehend it, but merely repeated in a dull, questioning tone: "Baldur the beautiful . . .?"

They shouldered him aside and bent over Baldur. The blind god clutched at them insistently, but they pushed him away. He heard them walking off slowly, as though they were carrying something. They were gone, leaving him alone in his darkness with no one to answer his call.

"We must bury Baldur gloriously," said Odin, "and send him down in fitting splendor to the gloomy kingdom of Hel. Yet while we mourn him, we will not despair. I have given my own untiring horse to Hermod, my messenger, and he has gone down through the mist to beg Hel for Baldur's life."

The gods sent Baldur to sea in a blazing pyre on the deck of his Viking ship. He had weapons and bright garments to take with him, and Odin gave him a ring, his greatest treasure, from which eight new rings dropped on each ninth night. All the gods and the Valkyries, and even the frost giants watched the vessel sail with its flaming burden straight out to the setting sun. But while they sorrowed for Baldur, Hermod was riding Odin's wind-swift horse down through the darkness nine nights long, until the green earth above him seemed a vague and distant dream. At last in a gleam of light he saw the deep, black river which bounded Hel's kingdom, and over it a bridge roofed with shining gold.

"Who rides my bridge?" cried the maiden who sat guarding it. "Five troops of dead who passed over yesterday did not shake it as does the tread of this one man."

"Has Baldur passed this way?" called Hermod.

"Baldur, the beautiful, rode downward and northward, where lies the palace of Hel."

Hermod sets spurs to Sleipnir, and the tireless horse rushed on over the grey rocks and the echoing valleys where nothing grew. They leaped the great wall around Hel's palace, and Hermod alighting, strode through her yawning doors.

Vast and grey was the palace of Hel, and the flames of her fire burned chilly blue. The goddess sat in a chair of bone. Her pale face was ghastly in the strange light, and her eyes stared like the eyes of the dead. Down the long table beside her sat shadowy hosts of men, some clothed in faint scarlet and misty gold, some in dim rags, all pale. Here the table they sat at was Famine, and the beds that they slept in were Care.

Baldur, the Beautiful

By the dreadful goddess sat Baldur, his golden hair faint and dull, yet still he turned to the messenger with the ghost of his lovely smile. He thanked him in tones like those of his own voice far away.

"Great goddess," cried Hermod loudly in the full voice of the living, "in pity give us back Baldur, without whom the whole world is forlorn."

Hel neither spoke nor moved her set eyes, but she turned her head around on him in a pitiless glare.

"Give us back Baldur," pleaded Hermod. "Never before has a living god or hero dared to make this ride."

His voice echoed through the great hall and died away into silence. All the ranks of grey dead sat staring at him, and Hel answered never a word.

"In the name of Allfather Odin, who set you here," cried Hermod again, "answer me and grant me Baldur, the darling of the earth."

"If all the world so loves Baldur," said Hel in a voice hoarse from long disuse, "then let all the earth weep. If all things mourn for Baldur, he may go free; but if one refuses, he shall remain."

The shade of Baldur rose from his place and accompanied Hermod to the door. "Give my greeting to Asgard," said he in his faroff, gentle voice. "It is a long way thence, and Hel will keep me, but when the Day of Doom and Destruction has passed over the earth, I shall arise to behold a new and more beautiful world."

"We shall deliver you," cried Hermod. "Be very sure that everything will weep."

Etching, by William Blake

"Take his ring to my father, Odin," said the shade, "in memory of me." He put the ring into Hermod's hand, where it glowed as bright and golden as it had done in Odin's hall. "Farewell, and remember Baldur."

All the earth wept for Baldur in running stream of tears. The trees and plants dripped gently, flowers folded, the air was misty, and the clouds dropped rain. All the birds fell silent, save the mourning dove and the melancholy nightingale. As the messengers of Odin went from place to place, the very stones oozed moisture, as they do in the spring thaw. At last, however, the gods came to a cave in the hills, in the mouth of which sat Loki, disguised as an aged hag. "Weep for Baldur!" cried they. "Only the tears of the whole world may unloose him from the bonds of Hel."

The hag looked up. "Why should I weep for Baldur?" she croaked. "What did he do for me?"

"Baldur, the beautiful, is the source of the whole world's joy. Weep for him, lest he vanish forever and leave sorrow and pain on earth."

"When did I ever rejoice?" cried Loki in the voice of the aged hag. "Let Hel keep what she has. Why should I care?" With a screech he sprang up and fled into the darkness of the cave, nor would he come forth again, no matter how the messengers implored.

Thus Hel kept her hold on Baldur, even as he had foreseen. With him pure goodness and joy vanished from earth. What remained was mixed with evil and haunted by care. Nevertheless, it was said that after the Day of Doom a new world would come. Then Baldur would arise from the dead and sit in the meadows with Hoder, no longer blind. The sons of Thor and Odin would dwell on the plains where Asgard had risen before, and a new, fair race would people the earth in the light of a brighter sun.

QUESTIONS FOR DISCUSSION

1. Recognizing that these ancient people wanted to explain the changes from summer to winter, what do you think Baldur, Hoder, and the death of Baldur represent?
2. This myth is divided into two parts. What is the high point, or climax, of the first part? Of the second? Could either part be an individual story? Why, or why not?
3. An author uses different devices to move the plot and create atmosphere. How many journeys were described? What were they? Why did the teller select the order that he did?

Baldur, the Beautiful

4. When Hermod reached Hel's palace, the mood of the story changed. How did the author establish the feeling of gloom and despair? Note the words used to describe the palace—"yawning doors," "vast and grey," and "fire burned chilly blue." What expressions were used to describe Hel? How had Baldur changed? Is a similar mood found elsewhere in the Norse myths? Give details.

5. The idea of fate, or destiny, appears in many myths. In what Greek myths did you encounter it? How did destiny determine Baldur's doom? Baldur was destined to arise after the Day of Doom. What, then, does he symbolize?

SUGGESTIONS FOR COMPOSITION

1. Select a scene from this myth and create a dramatic skit. You might, for example, choose Frigga's frantic efforts to save her son, or perhaps Hermod's return from the underworld.

2. Create a short poem based on the changes in nature that occurred when Baldur died. Read your efforts to the class.

The hour was at hand. The foretold Day of Doom was approaching: the Fenris Wolf lay howling and writhing in his bonds, Hel kept her hold on Baldur, and goodness and joy had vanished from the earth. The story of the ensuing battle is both awesome and terrifying.

The Twilight of the Gods

Olivia E. Coolidge

Year after year went by, and all the beings of creation, great and small, passed their days as they had always done. But there were those who did not forget what had been foretold since the beginning of time: that one day all of creation, as they knew it, would come to an end.

At last the Gods, looking down on the world from high Asgard, saw signs that the Day of Doom was near. The light of the sun grew dim and was no longer warm. At sunset the sky turned red as blood. Crops failed and food became scarce.

Woodcut, by Ernst Barlach

A harsh winter came, but it was not winter which would turn again into spring, summer, and the rich harvest of autumn. Instead, there were three winters in a row, during which snow fell continuously. Deadly frost killed the seeds in the ground and the roots of growing things. Terrible winds blew the snow across the ground and piled it in mountainous drifts. It did no good for men to ask heaven for relief. They starved, were frozen to death, and looked with dying eyes toward a sky that was forever gray with frost-bound clouds. They could scarcely remember when they had last seen the sun. What had long been foretold was upon them, and no power could stop it. This first time of winter was called the Age of the Winter Winds.

Three more winters followed, worse than the first three. Those few men who had survived turned against each other. Family ties were forgotten as brother murdered brother, fighting for the little food that was left, the scraps of firewood, a place in the small caves and corners of the world where the cold seemed not to chill so deeply. Their battles were useless and bitter. Vultures and wolves prowled in the storms, and the snow was stained red with blood. Not enough men were left to bury the dead, and they did not care about anything anymore except fighting for their own lives. It was an evil, lawless time, when no one cared any longer about justice, love, or duty. This was called the Age of the Sword.

The last times before the Day of Doom were called the Age of the Wolf. Deep in the Iron Wood sat the giantess who was mother of Loki's monster offspring. To the Wolf Managarm, destined to devour the moon, she fed the corpses of men. The wolf's tearing jaws splattered blood far and wide, even on the seats of the Gods, as the wolf grew sleek and powerful.

In Jotunheim, the giants were awakened by the crowing of Fialar, the red cock. This was a signal for them to prepare for the last combat.

A second cock crowed, deep in the halls of Hel, and the spirits of the underworld began to assemble.

In Asgard, a third cock crowed, a cock with a golden comb, called Gullinkambir. Gods and champions made ready for battle.

Garm the hound howled loudly deep in the earth, broke the chains that held him, and ran free.

All these things were signs that the end was near. Seeing them, Heimdall, doorkeeper of the gods, brought out his horn and blew a long, clear note. The gods and heroes listened. It was time.

Though he knew they were all doomed, Odin called on all his strength and wisdom to help him decide how they might meet the end most fittingly. He went to the Well of Wisdom and drew up Mimir's head. Weaving a spell by means of secret runes, he caused it to speak. "Where shall the Champions of Midgard meet?" he asked. "How shall we best battle the forces of evil and destruction?"

The head of Mimir answered, "Meet on Vigard Plain, for though your own world will be lost in the battle, there you will wage such a war that the powers of evil will be forever destroyed."

Suddenly the whole earth shook, as if in a violent earthquake. The Tree of Life, Yggdrasil, trembled, making a sound like moaning with its branches. Everywhere there was uproar and the sound of armies preparing for battle. At last the Fenris Wolf broke the bonds that had been woven to hold him so long ago. His jaws gaped wide, stretching from earth to sky. Again the hound Garm howled, a sound so mournful and far-reaching that even the strongest, both good and evil, shuddered to hear it.

The fiery spirits of Muspelheim mounted their horses and rode to battle, with Surtur leading them, his sword bright as the sun. Wherever they rode, flames caught and burned high. The riders of Muspelheim first began to cross Bifrost, the rainbow bridge leading to Asgard, but the bridge collapsed beneath them, and they turned downward instead toward Vigard Plain.

Then the Midgard Serpent rose out of the sea onto the shore, bringing a great flood. Streams, lakes, and rivers overran their banks.

The giants, led by Hymer, launched their ship Naglfar on the rushing water. Another ship sailed from Hel, piloted by Hymer and Loki, with the Fenris Wolf beside them on the deck.

Again the earth shook with even greater violence, and hills and mountains crumbled away. The Tree of Life shook and groaned, and the sky itself split in two. Once more Garm howled, as he rushed toward Vigard Plain, blood foaming on his jaws.

To gods and champions Odin said, "These are sorrowful days but we have no time for mourning. Instead, let us fight bravely. We will give our lives and let our world be destroyed, but we will battle so that these evil powers will not live after us." Then Odin sprang to challenge the Fenris Wolf, as the monster leaped from Hel's ship onto the plain. Odin fought fiercely, alone, but the huge jaws finally overcame him and he died, murdered by the Fenris Wolf.

Frey fought bravely against the fire-bright sword of Surtur, but he had given his own magic sword to Skirnir, and without it he was killed.

Thor leaped forward barely in time to stop Jormungand the Serpent from spraying deadly venom on them all. Singlehandedly, Thor crushed the beast with a blow from his hammer, but Thor himself died in the Serpent's jaws, seared and blinded by the serpent's poison.

Now Odin's son, Vidar, entering the battle along with the other younger gods, placed his foot on the Fenris Wolf's lower jaw, pinning it to the ground. With one hand he seized the wolf's upper jaw, and with the

The Twilight of the Gods

107

other drove his sword down the beast's throat, to its heart; Odin's death was avenged.

On all sides the combatants waged their battle to the death. Loki and Heimdall struggled against one another until both were dead. Tyr, as brave as when he had sacrificed his right hand so that the Fenris Wolf could be bound, killed many of the enemy with his strong left hand, but finally he died in the bloody jaws of the Hound Garm.

Onward rode Surtur at the head of the riders of Muspelheim. It seemed that nothing would stop them. Wherever they went, fire spread destruction. Even the branches of the Tree Yggdrasil caught fire, and the Tree of Life was destroyed. Fire shot up everywhere, like huge fountains of flame reaching as high as the heavens. Finally, even Surtur and his followers perished in their own fire.

Sol, the Sun, was eaten by the Wolf Hati; the Wolf Managarm devoured Maane, the Moon. The stars fell and their light vanished from the sky. The land sank beneath the water with a great hissing of steam, and foul-smelling smoke billowed above the waves. The world lay in utter darkness.

In that deep, unnatural night, the seas rolled across the ruined earth. It seemed that nothing remained, neither life nor hope, but only blackness and the moving sea.

Finally, after ages had passed, the waters parted and the green earth appeared again. Rivers ran in their courses as before. Eagles flew above them, hunting for fish in the upland streams.

A new sun and moon came to light the sky in peace. Grain sprang up on the empty land. Baldur and Hodur returned, as had been foretold.

Four of the younger gods remained: Vidar and Vali, sons of Odin, and Modi and Magni, sons of Thor. The gods met together and spoke of the times past, of the Midgard Serpent and the Fenris Wolf, of the doom of the old world, and of the wisdom of their fathers. They built a hall, called Gimli, and thatched its roof with gold that shone with such warmth and brightness it seemed the sun itself lived there. Here the gods would live forever in peace and prosperity.

Miraculously, two of mankind had survived the Day of Doom, a man and woman, Lif and Lifthrasir. They lay hidden in a deep sleep until the world was again ready for them. Then they awoke and made their first meal of the life-giving morning dew. From these two came a new race of men.

QUESTIONS FOR DISCUSSION

1. While coldness, loneliness, and hunger swept over the countryside, man himself changed in a corresponding fashion. Given this fact, how does the *setting* reflect the subject? What is the concrete subject? The abstract subject?
2. What was the order in which things were destroyed? Compare it with the ordering of events in "The Creation." Does the *form* reflect the subject in each? Support your answer with evidence from the myths.
3. The new world is perfect; evil no longer exists. Do you think myths about this new world would be as exciting as those about the old? Why?

A SUMMING UP

1. You have surely noticed that there are many similarities between Greek and Norse myths. Name some of the more notable ones. How do you account for these similarities?
2. There are important differences, too. What are some of them? Were the Norsemen's ideas influenced by the world they lived in? How did this affect their myths?
3. Is the point of view objective in both the Norse and Greek myths? Or did the teller allow his own personal view to creep into the stories?
4. Compare some of the Greek gods with the Norse gods. How did Zeus and Odin differ? Were they similar in some other ways? What does this tell us about the people who created these mythic rulers?
5. Which of the Norse myths most resemble the hero tales of the Greeks? Which myths seem mostly explanatory; which seem to be an attempt to explain natural phenomena?
6. Look back over the Norse myths. Note the order in which they are arranged. Is a general pattern apparent? Explain. What unifies these stories?
7. Does the definition of a myth, which you worked out earlier, fit this group of tales? In what ways?

SUGGESTED ACTIVITIES

1. Try writing a gossip column in which you cover some of the amusing and interesting activities of the Greek deities. Or, if you prefer, try writing a column of advice to gods and goddesses. You should have some fun in thinking of a title for your column.

2. Assume the personality of a god or goddess and write a letter to another deity, or you might like to exchange letters with a student who has assumed the personality of the god or goddess you have chosen to write to. What kind of letter might Rhea write to Gaia, for example? What would Hera write to Zeus when she was angry? The possibilities are unlimited.

3. Turn some of the myths you've read into news articles. Think up some typical headlines, like "War Rages in Heaven," or "Heracles Dead."

4. You might like to collect some of the articles you've been working on and, with the help of your teacher, publish an edition of the *Mt. Olympus News*.

5. Assume the identity of some god or goddess and write a journal or a diary, giving the day-by-day experiences you might encounter. Use your imagination, and when you have finished, read your diary over carefully. Does it seem to reflect the personality of the god or goddess? In what way?

6. Create a Greek or Norse hero and invent a quest for him. Tell his story briefly. Remember to use the pattern you found in the hero tales you read earlier.

7. Write a few short paragraphs in which you compare the lives and activities of the Greek deities with those of the Norse gods. You might consider covering some of the following points:

   a. Were the gods in both mythologies in human shape? How did they differ from humans? Did they possess unlimited powers?

   b. Were both Greek and Norse gods perfect? Or did they often possess bad as well as good qualities?

   c. How did they feel about humans?

   d. Were their family relationships harmonious, or did they frequently quarrel among themselves?

   e. Which ruler — Odin or Zeus — seemed the more responsible? Why?

8. Drawing upon class discussion and your own conclusions about the myths you have read, write a few paragraphs explaining, as you now see them, the distinguishing characteristics of the myth. Use examples.

9. You have now studied various kinds of folk narrative: the myth, the proverb, fable, and parable. You've talked about some of their differences in class; perhaps you've even written a paragraph in which you specifically pointed out some of their differences. Do they have similarities as well? Why do you think they are all referred to as "folk narratives"? Write a paragraph in which you point out some of the similarities among these various types of narrative. Be specific, giving examples from your reading whenever possible.

Aegir (e´ jir) sea god

Aesir (e´ sir) name for the horse family of gods

Asgard (äs´ gärd) home of the gods

Baldur (bôl´ dər) son of Odin and god of the sun

Bure (bûr´ ə) ancestor of the gods

Elle (ĕl´ ə) giant who symbolized old age

Freyja (frā´ yä) Odin's daughter

Frigga (frig´ ə) Odin's wife

Heimdall (hām´ däl) Odin's watch-man

Hel (hĕl) daughter of Loki; ruler of the underworld

Hermod (her´ müd) messenger

Hoder (hô´ dər) blind son of Odin and Frigga

Huge (h(y)ü´ jə) giant

Hymer (hī´ mir) giant who lost his caldron

Loge (lō´ gi) giant

Loki (lō´ kē) father of evil; Odin's son

Mjolnir (myœ l´ nir) Thor's hammer

Niflheim (niv˝ əl hām´) infernal region of mist and ice below the universe

Norns (nôrnz) the Fates, in the form of three veiled hags

Odin (ō´ din) ruler of the gods

Thjalfe (thyäl´ fə) mortal, accompanied Thor to Giantland

Thor (thôr) Odin's son, god of thunder and lightning

Tyr (tēr) Odin's son

Utgard-Loke (üt´ gärd lō´kē) king of Giantland

Valhalla (val hal´ ə) Odin's great hall

Valkyries (val kēr´ ēz) maiden warriors

Ymer (ē´ mir) first frost giant

African and Native American Myths and Legends

In any study of English and American literature, Greek and Norse mythologies must take a central place, simply because they are so frequently mentioned. But there is another reason for studying myths, folk-tales, fables, legends, and the like. As you read the stories of other peoples, you soon recognize a very important fact. All peoples in all lands tell the same sort of stories, to explain their beginnings or the reasons why things in nature are the way they are. Seeing the same story patterns repeated over and over again, you soon realize that human beings of all nations and races are more alike than they are different. In a world as full of differences as ours, it is important to realize that we are all basically the same. The myths and legends of all races show this.

We are giving you here just the briefest sample from the vast reservoir of African and Native American myths and legends. You will notice that some of them are shorter and less polished than the Greek and Norse stories you have read. This is because they have only recently been collected and written down, and have not had as much chance to be smoothed and re-written by other authors. You should be able to recognize familiar myth patterns in them, however, as these stories also attempt to deal with man's place in the world and why things are the way they are. Because there are so many stories and tribes from which to choose, we have included samples from several different areas of Africa and North America. Let us begin with a short African story of the creation of man.

The Story of Creation

Blaise Cendrars

Before anything at all was made, Mbere, the Creator, he made man out of clay. He took clay and he shaped it into a man. This was how man began, and he began as a lizard. This lizard, Mbere put it into a bowl of sea water. Five days, and this is what happened: five days passed with him in the bowl of water, and he had put him there, inside it. Seven days passed; he was in there for seven days. And the eighth day, Mbere took a look at him, and now the lizard came out; and now he was outside. But it was a man. And he said to the Creator: "Thank you!"

You will remember that Zeus hurled thunderbolts, and that Thor's hammer sounded like thunder. Here is a story from Nigeria which offers a different explanation for the same aspect of Nature.

Thunder and Lightning

Kathleen Arnott

A long time ago, both thunder and lightning lived on this earth, among all the people. Thunder was an old mother sheep and Lightning was her son, a handsome ram, but neither animal was very popular.

When anybody offended the ram, Lightning, he would fly into a furious rage and begin burning down huts and corn bins, and even knock down large trees. Sometimes he damaged crops on the farms with his fire and occasionally he killed people who got in his way.

As soon as his mother, Thunder, knew he was behaving in this evil way, she would raise her voice and shout as loudly as she could, and that was very loud indeed.

Naturally the neighbours were very upset, first at the damage caused by Lightning and then by the unbearable noise that always followed his outbursts. The villagers complained to the king on many occasions, until at last he sent the two of them to live at the very edge of the village, and said that they must not come and mix with people any more.

However, this did no good, since Lightning could still see people as they walked about the village streets and so found it only too easy to continue picking quarrels with them. At last the king sent for them again.

"I have given you many chances to live a better life," he said, "but I can see that it is useless. From now on, you must go right away from our village and live in the wild bush. We do not want to see your faces here again."

Thunder and Lightning had to obey the king and left the village, angrily cursing its inhabitants.

Alas, there was still plenty of trouble in store for the villagers, since Lighting was so angry at being banished that he now set fire to the whole bush, and during the dry season this was extremely unfortuante. The flames spread to the little farms which the people had planted, and sometimes to their houses as well, so that they were in despair again. They often heard the mother ram's mighty voice calling her son to order, but it made very little difference to his evil actions.

The king called all his councillors together and asked them to advise him, and at last they hit on a plan. One white-headed elder said:

"Why don't we banish Thunder and Lightning right away from the earth? Wherever they live there will be trouble, but if we sent them up into the sky, we should be rid of them."

So Thunder and Lightning were sent away into the sky, where the people hoped they would not be able to do any more damage.

Things did not work out quite as well as they had hoped, however, for Lightning still loses his temper from time to time and cannot resist sending fire down to the earth when he is angry. Then you can hear his mother rebuking him in her loud rumbling voice.

Ocassionally even his mother cannot bear to stay with him and goes away for a little while. You will know when this happens, for Lightning still flashes his fire on the earth, but his mother is so far away that she does not see, and her voice is silent.

Thunder and Lightning

115

Remember Prometheus's great gift of fire to man, and how Zeus punished him for it. Apparently fire has had great significance for all peoples. Here is an African story that has many similarities to the Greek myth: Notice that the god doesn't want man to have fire, and that the person who gives the gift is punished.

Since these stories come from different parts of Africa, the names of the gods change. But it doesn't really matter: Zeus, or Mbere, or Obassi Osaw, they are all the same: the chief god.

How Man Got Fire

Susan Bennett

In the beginning Obassi Osaw made all things on earth but he did not give fire to man. It was very cold and the people in the villages huddled together for warmth. Finally one of the chiefs cried out, "It is not fair. What is the use of Obassi Osaw putting us on earth if he will not give us fire to comfort ourselves?" He grabbed his youngest son and said, "Go to Obassi Osaw, tell him we must have fire!"

The boy made the journey but when he came to Obassi Osaw the god shook his head angrily. "Tell your father he is a fool," he yelled, and the boy went back to earth.

"I will go myself, then, you good-for-nothing boy," the father cried. "Obassi Osaw will listen to me!" But when the chief appealed to the god he too was sent home and then his son laughed. "Who are you to call yourself a chief? I will go back myself and if Obassi Osaw doesn't give me fire, this time I will steal it!"

Again the boy made the long journey and when he came to the compound of Obassi Osaw he went in and helped the wives get dinner. For many days he did not approach the god but made himself useful to all. One evening Obassi Osaw sent for him, "You seem trustworthy and helpful. Go to my third wife and bring back a lamp." The boy did as he was told and while he was getting the lamp he noticed that in this house the fire was stored. The next night Obassi Osaw again sent for him "Bring my light," he said, and the boy went forth. The wife was busy so she told the lad to light the lamp himself. The boy was excited. He lighted the lamp with a long, slender stick. Then he carefully wrapped the burning stick in leaves so that the fire would not go out, and hid it in the folds of his clothes. When

Wooden figure,
Bakota, West Sudan

he took the lamp to Obassi he suddenly doubled over as if in pain. "May I go out?" he asked the god, "I think I am going to be sick." Then he ran to the brush and hid the stick. That night as soon as it was dark and all were asleep he crept to the bush, and taking out the fire, he ran and ran until he once more reached earth.

He pulled the leaves from the burning stick and the flame lighted his face. "Bring me wood!" he cried with excitement. "I will show you how to use fire."

Obassi Osaw woke up sneezing. He looked around his compound but the fires were burning evenly; none of them were throwing out smoke. He looked down at the earth and then he understood. "Akpan," he called, "Akpan Obassi, go to earth and find out if it is the boy who has stolen our fire." Obassi's eldest son nodded and traveled to earth.

The boy confessed. "I stole it, and I am not sorry; we needed the fire here. You suffer no loss."

Akpan bowed, "I bring you a message from Obassi Osaw. You walked to heaven and took the fire; you walked back to earth. From this moment forth you will walk as one burned, not straight and proud but lame."

And so it has been. Lame boy cannot walk. He brought fire to earth from the home of Obassi Osaw.

How Man Got Fire

The Indians of North America have a mythology as rich and varied as do the peoples of Africa, Greece, or Scandinavia. Let us take a look at some of their stories dealing with already familiar myth themes — the creation of the world, why things are the way they are, and so forth. Here is a creation story from the Apache nation of the Southwestern United States.

How the People Sang the Mountain Up

Maria Leach

Silence. Dark. There was nothing there. Only the Hactcins, the Holy Ones, were there from the beginning. They owned the stuff of creation. There was no light — just darkness and the Hactcins creating things in the dark.

Black Hactcin was the great creator. He made all the animals and told them to walk, and they walked. He told the birds how to fly, and they flew. Hactcin created a man and told him to speak and to walk and to laugh. Then he made a woman. After that the people were many.

It was dark down there where the people lived because there was no sun. So Black Hactcin called for White Hactcin to come, because White Hactcin owned the sun stuff.

"The people need light," said Black Hactcin.

White Hactcin looked in his bag and took out a little sun.

"This will make daylight," he said.

Then Black Hactcin looked in his bag and took out a little moon.

"This can shine in the night," he said.

The sun and the moon were very small and dim.

"You had better start singing," said Black Hactcin.

So they sang together to make the sun and moon grow larger; and as they sang, the sun and moon began to grow; their light became strong and bright; and the sun and moon moved in their courses, just as they do today.

But it was still dim where the people were. The sun and moon were too far away, too high. What the people needed was a mountain.

Then the Hactcins made four little mounds of earth for the people.

In each one they hid the seeds and fruits which were to grow, and on top of each little mound they laid the leaves and needles of the trees which were to grow on the mountain.

The little mounds stood in a row, east to west. One was a little mound of black earth, one was of blue earth, one was yellow earth, and the fourth was glittering earth. All mountains are made of these four kinds of earth. Then the Hactcins filled a black clay bowl with water (because nothing can grow without water) and they watered the little mounds.

All the animals and birds and people were there and helped to make the mounds grow. They all sang and the mountain began to rise. They were all using their power.

They sang and sang, and the mountain grew and the fruits and trees began to grow on the mountain. They sang four times and the mountain grew, twelve times and the mountain grew twelve times. As it grew, the four little mounds merged together and grew into one big mountain. This spread into a long, beautiful range.

Then the people began traveling up the mountains. The birds flew up first, then came the animals and the people. They climbed and climbed and finally came forth into a sunny world.

When the people were all up the mountains in the sun, the Hactcins put a white pot upside down on top of the highest peak, so all would remember it forever. Some say it rises north of Durango, Colorado, one of the peaks of the San Juan Mountains.

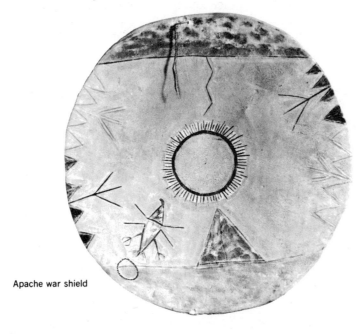

Apache war shield

*How the People
Sang the Mountain Up*

In the section of African myths you read a story about the origin of thunder and lighting. All mythologies are concerned with explaining natural events of all sorts. A famous Greek myth, the story of Persephone and Pluto, explains how the seasons came to be. You might want to look it up in your library, and compare it with this Cherokee version.

How the Seasons and the Birds Came

Princess Atalie

Children of the Red people snuggled close in their wigwams. Winter winds were cold and there were no changes of season. Days and nights were of unusual length, and the Red people and animals had one language. They ate only herbs, roots, and the flesh of small animals they were able to catch with their hands, so the Red men became hunters. Before they killed an animal they would offer a prayer to the Great Spirit, and apologize to the animal for taking his life because they deemed it a necessity.

A Council was called to decide upon the length of the days and nights, for the animals did not feel safe, and decided to declare war on the Red people.

Rabbit, who was a peace-loving little creature, happened along just then. He was known among the animals as a clever magician.

"I will go to the Thunder Spirit," he said, "and ask him to help us." He ran to the Thunder Spirit and told him that he wanted something for the Red people to plant.

The Thunder Spirit saw that all the animals would soon disappear if the Red people did not have other food to eat. He tapped on Mother Earth with his wand of witch-hazel. Tiny little green stalks shot from the earth. Rabbit was excited, and said, "May I take some of these to the Council for the Red people?"

"If you will eat a few in the presence of Owl, who is the judge, you may give these plants to the Red people," said the Thunder Spirit. Rabbit hastened to Owl, who was a very stern old judge. Although he was afraid, he hopped close to Owl's hollow tree and nibbled some of the green leaves.

Owl stared at him without blinking or closing his eyes. To this day he is known to stare with eyes open longer than any other living creature. Finally, he said, "The Red people would like to share your food."

Rabbit was so pleased that he gave one leap and returned to the mountain of the Thunder Spirit. The Thunder Spirit was expecting him, and sent him back to the Council with a load of the green stalks. Wherever Rabbit hopped an abundance of the green plants sprang up in the forest, and the Red people called it rabbit lettuce. Today lettuce is good for rabbits and man.

It was still very cold and the Red people longed for sunshine. The animals at the Council said they would try to bring Summer. Bear, however, became very angry, as he did not wish to have warm weather. He growled, "I will continue to give my flesh for food if you will let the winter stay." No one listened to Bear, for most of the animals were kind.

Wild Turkey strutted up, spreading his tail feathers, and gobbled, "The year shall have as many moons as there are spots on my tail."

But the members of the Council said, "No, that would make the year too long."

Then Partridge said, "Count my spots, and divide your year by their number." But the council declined that suggestion too.

A tiny chattering voice then said, "I am Chipmunk, and I insist that there be as many moons as there are stripes on my back." There were six black stripes and six white stripes on his back. The Councillors said that that number was about right; the white stripes would represent the summer moons, and the black stripes the winter moons. Bear did not approve of this and jumped at Chipmunk to crush him, but Chipmunk was too swift for him and ran to safety, saying, "You are the cause of my having these stripes. Your claws scratched me when I said I was for the warm weather." Bear went away in anger, growling, "Whoever gets my flesh for food will have to catch me!" He ran away in the forest of the far North, and to this day Bear is difficult to catch.

Other wild creatures of the forest wished to help the Red people. Frog made a long trip to Ha-shootch-ga, and told him that he also wished to make a gift of food to the Red people. The Thunder Spirit saw a plant with a little pointed top growing in the woods. He sent a drop of rain into Owl's eye and caused him to lessen his stare, while Frog quickly uprooted one of these plants. Frog then hopped down toward the Council, holding the plant over his head like an umbrella. Wherever he leaped, other little umbrellas grew from the earth, and in this way the first mushrooms came, giving food to man.

Wild Turkey came to Council with a plant whose roots were peas. She strutted up to Owl and said, "Thunder Spirit said for the Red people to plant these and grow many more peas." She scratched in the earth and left them there. Turkey peas grew in abundance. The Red people have been digging in the woods ever since for Turkey peas.

Now the Red People had plants for food, but Winter still covered the land. This was because O-kee, who was an evil spirit, was afraid that the Red people would climb the wall of the sky and destroy his dark and dreary days. So he turned a beautiful lake into a caldron of fat and decreed

Mythology

that whoever could swim across should find a land of warm sunshine. Red people and the animals all jumped into the lake. Some were swift in swimming across and they remained very lean. Some were slow in swimming and they became very fat. That is why some people and some animals are fat and others are lean.

Rabbit was the first to cross the lake. He came to the wall of the sky and disappeared. Red people were amazed at this. One of the young braves said, "I will follow Rabbit and see what lies beyond the sky wall. When I return I will be able to tell you many wondrous things."

The journey through the sky was dangerous. No Red man had ever entered its gardens before and returned. It was said to have birds of gorgeous plumage, golden fruits, and green grass. But one had to pass O-kee first. The brave followed Rabbit and opened four closed doors. When he opened the first, a bird of paradise flew out, then a great eagle flew out. It circled high and low and beat its wings against the other doors. They, too, opened, and vast flocks of smaller birds flew in every direction. The brave looked at them in great astonishment. He had never seen so many birds before. He spoke to them, "Beautiful birds, fly to the earth and give my people courage and sunshine."

Eagle gathered the birds into families, all but the bird of Paradise. He preferred it to remain aloof and find refuge in enchanted places. Eagle directed other birds to fly in flocks. The cedar birds, the chickadees, the woodpeckers, and the snow birds gathered in one flock; they were to be

How the Seasons and Birds Came

123

winter birds. The song sparrows, meadow larks, blackbirds, and robins gathered in one flock; they were the spring birds. The crows, wild geese, sparrows, and blue jays gathered in one flock; they were the autumn birds. With a rush of wings, they flew through the hole in the sky on their way to the earth people.

O-kee knew that he was defeated. He rushed to the hole in the sky and closed it just as the young brave was climbing through.

"I will make you a prisoner of the sky. You shall look down on the earth only at noon," grumbled O-kee as he seized the brave with his long fingers. The young brave was turned into the great round sun that now fills the hole in the sky.

Today when the Red people see the sun they say, "There is the brave who took away our winter and sent us sunshine and warm days, with birds for every season."

Here is a myth about the origin of fire from a tribe of the Nez Perce Indians of the Pacific Northwest, who called themselves the Nimipu. See if you can recognize any similarities between this story and other myths you have read about the origin of fire. Can you think of any reason why the gods might not want man to have fire, and why the person who brings if to them is always punished?

The Origin of Fire

Ella E. Clark

Long ago the Nimipu had no fire. They could see fire in the sky sometimes, but it belonged to the Great Power. He kept it in great black bags in the sky. When the bags bumped into each other, there was a crashing, tearing sound, and through the hole that was made fire sparkled.

People longed to get it. They ate fish and meat raw as the animals do. They ate roots and berries raw as the bears do. The woman grieved when they saw their little ones shivering and blue with cold. The medicine men beat on their drums in their efforts to bring fire down from the sky, but no fire came.

At last a boy just beyond the age for the sacred vigil said that he would get the fire. People laughed at him. The medicine men angrily complained, "Do you think that you can do what we are not able to do?"

But the boy went on and made his plans. The first time that he saw the black fire bags drifting in the sky, he got ready. First he bathed, brushing himself with fir branches until he was entirely clean and was fragrant with the smell of fir. He looked very handsome.

With the inside bark of cedar he wrapped an arrowhead and placed it beside his best and largest bow. On the ground he placed a beautiful white shell that he often wore around his neck. Then he asked his guardian spirit to help him reach the cloud with his arrow.

All the people stood watching. The medicine men said among themselves, "Let us have him killed, lest he make the Great Power angry."

But the people said, "Let him alone. Perhaps he can bring the fire down. If he does not, then we can kill him."

The boy waited until he saw that the largest fire bag was over his head, growling and rumbling. Then he raised his bow and shot the arrow straight upward. Suddenly, all the people heard a tremendous crash, and they saw a flash of fire in the sky. Then the burning arrow, like a falling star, came hurtling down among them. It struck the boy's white shell and there made a small flame.

Shouting with joy, the people rushed forward. They lighted sticks and dry bark and hurried to their tipis to start fires with them. Children and old people ran around, laughing and singing.

When the excitement had died down, people asked about the boy. But he was nowhere to be seen. On the ground lay his shell, burned so that it showed the fire colors. Near it lay the boy's bow. People tried to shoot with it, but not even the strongest man and the best with bow and arrow could bend it.

The boy was never seen again. But his abalone shell is still beautiful, still touched with the colors of flame. And the fire he brought from the black bag is still in the center of each tipi, the blessing of every home.

Many myths explain why animals and birds behave the way they do. Here is a story form the Modoc Indians explaining why the bat flies alone at night. Notice that here, as in other myths, there are elements of the fable. The animals speak and have human characteristics; and in this story there is a moral implied. What do you think it might be?

Why the Bat Flies Alone

Maria Leach

Once long ago in the war between the animals and birds, Bat was fighting on the side of the birds. In that battle the animals won.

When Bat saw that the animals were winning, he hid under a log and waited. When the battle was over and it was time to go home, Bat went along with the animals.

"What are you coming for?" said the animals. "You were fighting for the birds."

"Oh I'm not a bird," said Bat. "Look, I have teeth. Whoever saw a bird with teeth?"

So they let Bat come along.

Later the animals and birds had another battle, and Bat was fighting on the side of the animals. This time the birds won the battle.

When Bat saw that the birds were winning, he hid under a log and waited. When the battle was over and it was time to go home, Bat went along with the birds.

"What are you doing here?" said the birds. "You were fighting against us!"

"Oh, I am not one of the animals," said Bat. "Look! I have wings. Animals do not have wings."

So they let Bat come along.

Later on, the animals and birds realized that Bat had joined first one side, then the other. So nobody wanted him.

"Henceforth, you fly alone at night," they said; and that is what Bat does.

Antonio Frasconi, 1954

*Why the Bat
Flies Alone*

127

GREEK MYTHS

Asimov, Isaac, *Words From the Myths*. Houghton Mifflin Co. 1961.

Colum, Padraic, *The Adventure of Odysseus and the Tale of Troy*, ill. by Willy Pogany. The Macmillan Co., 1918.

Colum, Padraic, *The Golden Fleece and the Heroes Who Lived Before Achilles*, The Macmillan Co., 1959.

Coolidge, Olivia, *Greek Myths*. Houghton Mifflin Co., 1949.

Graves, Robert, *The Siege and Fall of Troy*, ill. by Walter Hodges. Doubleday & Co., 1962.

——————, *Greek Gods and Heroes*. Doubleday & Co., 1960.

Hawthorne, Nathaniel, *A Wonder Book and Tanglewood Tales*. Dodd, Mead & Co., 1934.

Watson, Jane Werner, *The Iliad and the Odyssey*, ill. by Willy Pogany. The Macmillan Co., 1962.

NORSE MYTHS

Baldwin, James, *The Story of Siegfried*, ill. by Peter Hurd. Charles Scribner's Sons, 1931.

Coolidge, Olivia, *Legends of the North*. Houghton Mifflin Co., 1951.

Hosford, Dorothy C., *Sons of the Volsungs*, ill. by Frank Dobias. Holt, Rinehart and Winston, 1949.

Setlew, Catherine, *Adventures With the Heroes*, ill. by Steele Savage. Little, Brown, 1954. (Stories of Volsungs and the Nibelungs.)

EPICS YOU MIGHT ENJOY

Baldwin, James *The Story of Roland*, ill. by Peter Hurd. Charles Scribner's Sons, 1930.

Gaer, Joseph, *The Adventures of Rama*, ill. by Randy Monk. Little, Brown, 1954.

Mukerji, Dhan Gopal, *Rama, the Hero of India*. E. P. Dutton, 1930.

Sutcliff, Rosemary, *Beowulf,* ill. by Charles Keeping. E. P. Dutton, 1962.

Folktales

You have already studied several kinds of folk narratives. Now you will discover another and especially delightful variety —the folktale, or the wonder tale, as it is sometimes called. Actually, you have probably heard versions of folktales for as long as you can remember. "Cinderella" and "Snow White," for example, are a part of our culture. They are among the very few stories that you can expect almost everybody to know.

What you might not know is that these folktales belong to an enormous body of folk narratives that in many cases have outlasted several civilizations and are still being told and enjoyed today. The folktale has, in fact, entered into the mainstream of modern literature. For instance, did you ever hear of some

129

person's career referred to as going from "rags-to-riches"? That is the Cinderella motif. Have you ever been made to feel foolish and stupid and then had a daydream in which you proved to everybody that you weren't? Certainly you have, and so has everybody else. Perhaps that's why stories about the "stupid Hans" or "ugly duckling" appeal to so many people. You will be studying both of these folktale motifs in this unit.

Some years ago a movie entitled *The Treasure of the Sierra Madre* was chosen as the best film of the year. It had been adapted from a modern novel by the same name. What no one mentioned, however, was that an English poet named Geoffrey Chaucer some six hundred years before had told the same story in his *Canterbury Tales*. Rudyard Kipling used the same tale in "The King's Ankus." And there is also a version in the *Jatakas*, Buddhist stories of ancient Asia, well over two thousand years old! This serves to illustrate not only how an ancient tale has been used by modern authors, but also to suggest how universal folktales are. Different versions of the same tales are to be found in Japan, South America, Australia, and Missouri, among other places.

We can only wonder who first created these tales—and when. Indeed, people who have studied them are still puzzled about their age and their origins. Egyptian records contain some of the earliest folktales— and these were written long before the birth of Christ. In early Indian, Persian, Greek, and Hebrew writings we can find traces of the folktale more than two thousand years old.

It was not until the end of the seventeenth century, however, that European writers began to collect and write down these tales. Charles Perrault of France collected a group in 1697, and somewhat later the Grimm brothers of Germany recorded a large number.

In this unit, you will be reading folktales from several different nations and several different periods in history. As you read, keep a couple of things in mind. First, how do these tales resemble each other, and how do they differ? Which is more significant: their similarities or their differences? At the end of the unit, you will be asked what you think the general subject of a folktale is, so you might begin to think about that now, too.

THE CINDERELLA MOTIF

Do you recall the first time you ever heard the story of Cinderella? Most of us do not; we have simply known it for as long as we can remember. This is one of the most ancient and most widely circulated folktales in the world. No one really knows who told it first, or what nation it comes from originally. The earliest record in writing is found in China, A.D. 863. Europeans first recorded it in 1558, but inscriptions prove it was known in Iceland over one thousand years ago. Today there are hundreds of versions of this tale, from Europe to the Orient, from Africa to South America.

As you read, note how these tales differ from the version you know. Despite this, how are they clearly recognizable as Cinderella stories?

This tale has the chill of a Russian winter about it which lends a special charm to the age-old story of Cinderella. Note especially the rhythm of the language and the repetition. What effect do these features have?

Jack Frost

Jack Frost

There was once a stepmother who had a stepdaughter and a daughter of her own. At anything her own daughter did, the woman would pat her head and say: "Clever girl!" But no matter how hard the stepdaughter tried, she was always found in the wrong. Yet the truth of the matter was that the stepdaughter was as good as gold; in the proper hands she would have been like cheese in butter, but in her stepmother's house she bathed in tears every day. What could she do? Even an angry wind subsides at last; but when the old woman got angry she never quieted down, she would hurl one insult after another, and her mouth was so full of venom that her teeth itched.

One day the stepmother made up her mind to drive her stepdaughter out of the house. She said to her husband: "Take her, take her, old man, take her wherever you wish, so that my eyes do not see her and my ears do not hear her. And don't take her to the warm house of your kin, but into the open field in the bitter frost." The old man began to grieve and lament; none the less he put his daughter on a sledge. He wanted to cover

131

her with a horse cloth but did not dare. He took the homeless girl into the open field, set her down on a heap of snow, made the sign of the cross over her, and hastened home as fast as possible, that his eyes might not behold his daughter's death.

The poor little thing remained there shivering and softly repeating her prayers. Jack Frost came leaping and jumping and casting glances at the lovely maiden. "Maiden, maiden, I am Jack Frost the Ruby-nosed!" he said. "Welcome, Jack Frost! God must have sent you to save my sinful soul." Jack Frost was about to crack her body and freeze her to death, but he was touched by her wise words, pitied her, and tossed her a fur coat. She put it on, squatted on her heels, and sat thus. Again Jack Frost the Ruby-nosed came leaping and jumping and casting glances at the lovely maiden. "Maiden, maiden, I am Jack Frost the Ruby-nosed!" he said. "Welcome, Jack Frost! God must have sent you to save my sinful soul." But Jack Frost had not come to save her soul at all; he brought her a coffer,[1] deep and heavy, full of bedding and petticoats and all sorts of things for her dowry. And she sat on the coffer in her fur coat, so gay, so pretty! Again Jack Frost came leaping and jumping and casting glances at the lovely maiden. She welcomed him and he gave her a robe embroidered with silver and gold. She put it on—and how beautiful and stately she looked! She sat there happily singing songs.

Meanwhile her stepmother was preparing her funeral dinner and frying pancakes. "Go, husband," she said, "bring home your daughter, that we may bury her." The old man went. The little dog under the table said: "Bow-wow, the old man's daughter is coming home all decked in gold and silver, but no suitor wants the old woman's daughter!" "Be quiet, you fool! Here is a pancake for you, and now say that suitors will come for the old woman's daughter, but of the old man's daughter only bones will be brought home." The little dog ate the pancake and said again: "Bow-wow! The old man's daughter is coming home all decked in gold and silver, but the suitors don't want the old woman's daughter." The old woman gave the dog more pancakes and beat him, but he kept saying the same thing: "The

Folktales

[1]*coffer:* a chest.

old man's daughter is coming home decked in gold and silver, but the suitors don't want the old woman's daughter."

The gate creaked, the doors flew wide open, a coffer deep and heavy was brought in, and the stepdaughter followed, radiant, like a grand lady. The stepmother looked at her and threw up her arms. "Old man, old man," she ordered, "harness other horses, take my daughter at once, put her in the same field, in the very same place!" The old man took the girl to the same field and left her in the very same place. And Jack Frost the Ruby-nosed came, looked at his guest, leapt and jumped, but did not hear any kind words. He grew angry, seized her, and killed her. The old woman said to her husband: "Old man, go bring my daughter. Harness spirited horses —and don't overturn the sledge, don't drop the coffer!" But the little dog under the table said: "Bow-wow, the suitors will take the old man's daughter, but the bones of the old woman's daughter will be brought home in a sack." "Don't lie! here is a pancake for you, and say: 'The old woman's daughter is coming home decked in gold and silver.'" The gate flew open and the old woman ran out to greet her daughter, but instead she embraced a cold corpse. She began to wail and howl, but it was too late.

This story comes from an ancient book of Chinese tales by Tuan Ch'eng-shih, who died in A.D. 863. This apparently is the earliest written version of the Cinderella tale. Tuan said that this story was told him by a servant. As you read, note the chief characteristics of this little Chinese Cinderella. Is she similar to the Cinderella with whom you are familiar?

Cinderella (Chinese)

Lin Yutang

Once, before the time of Chin (222–206 B.C.) and Han, there was a chief of a mountain cave whom the natives called Cave Chief Wu. He married two women, one of whom died leaving him a baby girl named Yeh Hsien. She was very intelligent and clever at working on gold and her father loved her dearly, but when he died she was maltreated by her

stepmother who often forced her to cut wood and sent her to dangerous places to draw water from deep wells.

One day, Yeh Hsien caught a fish more than two inches long with red fins and golden eyes and she brought it home and placed it in a basin of water. Every day it grew bigger and bigger until the bowl could not hold it any longer, and she placed it in a pond back of her home. Yeh Hsien used to feed it with what she had saved from her own food. When she came to the pond, the fish would rise to the surface and pillow its head on the bank, but if anyone else came to the water's edge it would not appear.

This curious behavior was noticed by the stepmother who often waited for the fish, but it would never come up. One day she resorted to a ruse and said to the girl, "Are you not tired from work? I will give you a new jacket." Then she made Yeh Hsien take off her old clothing, and sent her off to a distance of several hundred *li* to draw water from another well. The mother then put on Yeh Hsien's dress, and hiding a sharp knife in her sleeve, went to the pond and called to the fish. When the fish put its head out of the water, she killed it. The fish was by that time over ten feet long, and when it was cooked, it tasted many times better than any other fish. And the mother buried its bones in a dunghill.

Next day, Yeh Hsien came back, and when she arrived at the pond, she saw that the fish was gone. Thereupon she wept until a man with disheveled hair, dressed in a ragged garment, descended from the sky and comforted her, saying, "Do not cry. Your mother has killed the fish, and its bones are buried under a dunghill. Go home and carry the bones to your room and hide them. Whatever you shall want, pray to them and your wish will be granted." Yeh Hsien followed his advice, and it was not long before she had gold and jewelry and finery of such costly texture that they would have delighted the heart of any young maiden.

The night of the Cave Festival Yeh Hsien was told to stay at home and watch the fruit orchard. When the lonely girl saw that her mother had gone a long distance, she arrayed herself in a green silk jacket and went to the festival. Her sister who had recognized her said to the mother, "Is that girl not strangely like my elder sister?" The mother also seemed to recognize her. When Yeh Hsien became aware of their glances she ran away, but in such haste that she dropped one of her slippers, which fell into the hands of the cave people.

When the mother came back home, she found her daughter sleeping with her arms around a tree. She put aside any suspicions she may have had about the identity of the finely dressed girl.

Now near the caves there was an island kingdom called T'o Huan. Through its strong army, it ruled over twenty-four islands, and its territorial waters covered several thousand *li*. The cave people therefore sold the slipper to the T'o Huan Kingdom, where it found its way to the king. The king made the women of his household try it on, but the slipper was an inch too short even for those who had the smallest feet. Then he had all of the women of the kingdom try it, but the slipper would fit none of them.

The king suspected the cave man of getting the slipper from dubious sources and imprisoned and tortured him. The unfortunate man could not tell where the shoe came from. Finally it was placed by the roadside and couriers were sent from house to house to arrest anyone who had the other slipper. The king was greatly puzzled.

All houses were searched and Yeh Hsien was found. She was made to put the slippers on, and they fitted her perfectly. She then appeared in her slippers and her green silk dress, looking like a goddess. Then a report was made to the king, and the king brought Yeh Hsien to his island home, together with her fishbones.

After Yeh Hsien had left the cave, the mother and sister were killed by flying stones. The cave people pitied them and buried them in a pit, erecting a tomb which they called "The Tomb of Regretful Women." The cave people worshiped them as the goddesses of matrimony, and whoever asked them a favor regarding marriage was sure to have her prayer granted.

The king returned to his island and made Yeh Hsien his first wife. During the first year of their marriage, he asked the fishbones for so many jades and precious things that they refused any longer to grant his wishes.

Cinderella (Chinese)

135

He then took the bones and buried them close by the sea, with a hundred bushes of pearls, lined with a border of gold. When his soldiers rebelled against him, he went to the spot, but the tide had washed them away and they have never been found to this day.

      This story was told me by an old servant of the family, Li Shih-yuan. He comes from the cave people of Yungchow, and remembers many strange stories of the South.

QUESTIONS FOR DISCUSSION

1. The tales you have just read are quite different from each other, yet all are about the same thing. In a short paragraph, state their common subject.
2. In the Grimm Brother's version of Cinderella, which we are all familiar with, everything that happens more or less leads up to the losing of the slipper. After that, all the action leads toward the day of triumph. You could even diagram it. The plot of Cinderella is something like a mountain climber; it goes up to a summit (the slipper) and down again, like this:

    See how the versions you have just read compare with this. Make a similar diagram for each. What will take the place of the slipper in the Russian version?

3. Cinderella's reversal in fortune—from poor to rich—is followed in both tales by another kind of reversal. As good luck brings wealth and happiness to Cinderella, what happens to her opposition? Do you find poetic justice in the two folktales you have just read?
4. The fairy godmother of the Cinderella you are familiar with is replaced in these tales. By what? Does this change affect the basic structure of the story?
5. Sometimes we say the *subject* of a story cannot be separated from its *form* or *point of view*. Don't forget that how a writer says something is part of what he says. Can you explain how the stepmother's dislike of Cinderella is really a part of the subject?

6. Compare the various attitudes of the people in these stories. Remember, the people you are reading about are of quite different nationalities —one is a Chinese girl whose story was first told over two thousand years ago, and the other is a Russian peasant girl.

    a) How did the stepmother in "Jack Frost" feel about her own daughter? Compare her actions with the actions of the Chinese stepmother.

    b) We discover a little more about the Prince (King) in the Chinese version than in the Russian. Is he completely admirable? How does he regard Cinderella's magic fish?

7. Quite often a folktale employs supernatural beings to help characters win out over really terrible circumstances. The behavior of the characters, however, usually makes them worthy of this supernatural assistance. Look back over "Jack Frost." Did the girl do or say anything that made her appear deserving of help? Discuss Yeh Hsien's treatment of the fish. Watch for such action in the other tales you read, too.

SUGGESTIONS FOR COMPOSITION

1. Have you ever read a rags-to-riches story or seen a film with such a subject? If so, write a paragraph explaining what similarities you see between the folktale and the story. Not all Cinderellas are girls; there are many stories about boys on whom Fortune has also smiled unexpectedly.

2. Why not try creating your own version of Cinderella, tailored to fit today's world. Make whatever substitutions you like and select incidents to illustrate your rags-to-riches theme.

THE BEAUTY AND THE BEAST MOTIF

    People have always delighted in the idea that in some miraculous way they might be transformed into other beings. Evidently people today are just as intrigued with the idea, if we are to judge by the number of science-fiction stories and television scripts which show how man, through some sort of scientific hocus-pocus, assumes another shape or makes himself invisible altogether.

    The following tales come from England and Russia. Despite this fact, they are quite similar. Compare them as you read.

You are about to meet an extraordinary dog, which has, along with its small teeth, a castle and great wealth. This is an English version—and a pleasantly homely one—of the famous Beauty and the Beast type of folktale.

The Small-Tooth Dog

Once upon a time, there was a merchant who traveled about the world a great deal. On one of his journeys thieves attacked him, and they would have taken both his life and his money if a large dog had not come to his rescue and driven the thieves away. When the dog had driven the thieves away he took the merchant to his house, which was a very handsome one, and he dressed his wounds and nursed him until he was well.

As soon as he was able to travel the merchant began his journey home, but before starting he told the dog how grateful he was for his kindness, and asked him what reward he could offer in return, and he said he would not refuse to give him the most precious thing that he had.

And so the merchant said to the dog, "Will you accept a fish that I have that can speak twelve languages?"

"No," said the dog, "I will not."

"Or a goose that lays golden eggs?"

"No," said the dog, "I will not."

"Or a mirror in which you can see what anybody is thinking about?"

"No," said the dog, "I will not."

"Then what will you have?" said the merchant.

"I will have none of such presents," said the dog, "but let me fetch your daughter, and take her to my house."

When the merchant heard this he was grieved, but what he had promised had to be done, so he said to the dog, "You can come and fetch my daughter after I have been at home for a week."

So at the end of the week the dog came to the merchant's house to fetch his daughter, but when he got there he stayed outside the door, and would not go in. But the merchant's daughter did as her father told her, and came out of the house dressed for a journey and ready to go with the dog.

When the dog saw her he looked pleased, and said, "Jump on my back, and I will take you away to my house." So she mounted on the dog's back, and away they went at a great pace until they reached the dog's house, which was many miles off.

But after she had been a month at the dog's house she began to mope and cry.

"What are you crying for?" said the dog.

The Small-Tooth Dog

139

"Because I want to go back to my father," she said.

The dog said, "If you will promise me that you will not stay at home more than three days I will take you there. But first of all," said he, "what do you call me?"

"A great, foul, small-tooth dog," said she.

"Then," said he, "I will not let you go."

But she cried so pitifully that he promised again to take her home. "But before we start," said he, "tell me what you call me."

"Oh!" said she, "your name is Sweet-as-a-honeycomb."

"Jump on my back," said he, "and I'll take you home." So he trotted away with her on his back for forty miles, when they came to a stile.

"And what do you call me?" said he, before they got over the stile.

Thinking that she was safe on her way, the girl said, "A great, foul, small-tooth dog." But when she said this, he did not jump over the stile, but turned right round about at once, and galloped back to his own house with the girl on his back.

Another week went by, and again the girl wept so bitterly that the dog promised to take her to her father's house. So the girl got on the dog's back again, and they reached the first stile as before, and then the dog stopped and said, "And what do you call me?"

"Sweet-as-a-honeycomb," she replied.

So the dog leaped over the stile, and they went on for twenty miles until they came to another stile.

"And what do you call me?" said the dog, with a wag of his tail.

She was thinking more of her own father and her own home than of the dog, so she answered, "A great, foul, small-tooth dog."

Then the dog was in a great rage, and he turned right round about and galloped back to his own house as before. After she had cried for another week, the dog promised again to take her back to her father's house. So she mounted upon his back once more, and when they got to the first stile, the dog said, "And what do you call me?"

"Sweet-as-a-honeycomb," she said.

So the dog jumped over the stile, and away they went — for now the girl made up her mind to say the most loving things she could think of—until they reached her father's house.

When they got to the door of the merchant's house, the dog said, "And what do you call me?"

Just at that moment the girl forgot the loving things that she meant to say, and began, "A great . . ." but the dog began to turn, and she got fast

140

hold of the door-latch, and was going to say "foul," when she saw how grieved the dog looked and remembered how good and patient he had been with her, so she said, "Sweeter-than-a-honeycomb."

When she had said this she thought the dog would have been content and have galloped away, but instead of that he suddenly stood up on his hind legs, and with his fore legs he pulled off his dog's head, and tossed it high in the air. His hairy coat dropped off, and there stood the handsomest young man in the world, with the finest and smallest teeth you ever saw.

Of course they were married, and lived together happily.

There are numerous varieties of frogs, but the one that returned Prince Ivan's arrow is not described in any zoologist's handbook. This Russian tale reverses the role of hero and heroine. Usually it is the girl who discovers that some ugly beast is really a handsome man. This time, however, it's a stalwart Russian prince who discovers that he should not judge all books by their covers, or all frogs by their skin.

The Frog Princess

Long ago, in ancient times, there was a king who had three sons, all of them grown. The king said: "My children, let each of you make a bow for himself and shoot an arrow. She who brings back your arrow will be your bride; he whose arrow is not brought back will not marry." The eldest son shot his arrow, and a prince's daughter brought it back to him. The middle son shot his arrow, and a general's daughter brought it back to him. But little Prince Ivan's arrow was brought back from the marsh by a frog who held it between her teeth. His brothers were joyous and happy, but Prince Ivan became thoughtful and wept: "How will I live with a frog? After all, this is a life task, not like wading across a river or walking across a field!" He wept and wept, but there was no way out of it, so he took the frog to wife. All three sons and their brides were wed in accordance with the customs of their country; the frog was held on a dish.

They began living together. One day the king asked that all three brides make him gifts, so that he could see which of them was the most

skillful. Prince Ivan again became thoughtful and wept: "What can my frog make? Everyone will laugh at me!" The frog only hopped about on the floor and croaked. When Prince Ivan fell asleep, she went out into the street, cast off her skin, turned into a lovely maiden, and cried: "Nurses, nurses! Make something!" The nurses at once brought a finely woven shirt. She took it, folded it, placed it beside Prince Ivan, and again turned herself into a frog, as though she had never been anything else! Prince Ivan awoke, was overjoyed with the shirt, and brought it to the king. The king received it, examined it, and said: "Well, this is indeed a shirt to wear on holidays!" Then the second brother brought a shirt. The king said: "This one is good only to wear to the bath!" And of the shirt the eldest brother brought he said: "This one is fit to be worn only in a lowly peasant hut!" The king's sons left, and the two elder ones decided between themselves: "We were wrong to make fun of Prince Ivan's wife; she is not a frog, but a cunning witch!"

142

The king again issued a command to his daughters-in-law—this time that they should bake bread, and show it to him, so that he might see which of them baked best. Before the first contest, the brides of the two elder sons had made fun of the frog; but now they sent a chambermaid to spy on her and see how she would go about baking her loaf. The frog was aware of this, so she mixed her dough, rolled it, hollowed out the oven from above, and poured her dough right there. The chambermaid saw this and ran to tell her mistresses, who forthwith did the same. But the cunning frog had deceived them; the moment the chambermaid left, she dug the dough out of the oven, cleaned and plastered up everything as though nothing had happened, then went on the porch, got out of her frog's skin, and cried: "Nurses, nurses! Bake me such a loaf of bread as my dear father ate only on Sundays and holidays!" The nurses brought the bread at once. She took it, placed it beside the sleeping Prince Ivan, and turned into a frog again. Prince Ivan awoke, took the bread, and went with it to his father. Just then the king was examining the loaves of bread brought by his elder sons. Their wives had dropped the dough into the oven just as the frog had, and all they had pulled out was formless lumps. First the king took the eldest son's loaf, looked at it, and sent it back to the kitchen; then he took the second son's loaf and sent it back too. Then came Prince Ivan's turn: he presented his loaf. The father received it, examined it, and said: "Now this bread is good enough for a holiday! It is not slack-baked, like that of my elder daughters-in-law!"

After that the king decided to hold a ball in order to see which of his daughters-in-law danced best. All the guests and the daughters-in-law assembled, and also the sons, except Prince Ivan, who became thoughtful: how could he go to a ball with a frog? And our Prince Ivan began to sob. The frog said to him: "Weep not, Prince Ivan! Go to the ball. I will join you in an hour." Prince Ivan was somewhat heartened when he heard the frog's words; he left for the ball, and the frog cast off her skin, and dressed herself in marvelous raiment. She came to the ball; Prince Ivan was over-joyed, and all the guests clapped their hands when they beheld her: what a beauty! The guests began to eat and drink; the princess would pick a bone and put it in her sleeve; she would drink of a cup and pour the last drops into her other sleeve. The wives of the elder brothers saw what she did, and they too put the bones in their sleeves, and whenever they drank of a cup, poured the last drops into their other sleeves. The time came for dancing; the tsar called upon his elder daughters-in-law, but they deferred to the frog. She straightway took Prince Ivan's arm and came forward to dance.

She danced and danced, and whirled and whirled, a marvel to behold! She waved her right hand, and lakes and woods appeared; she waved her left hand, and various birds began to fly about. Everyone was amazed. She finished dancing, and all that she had created vanished. Then the other daughters-in-law came forward to dance. They wanted to do as the frog had done: they waved their right hands, and the bones flew straight at the guests; and from their left sleeves water spattered, that too on the guests. The king was displeased by this and cried: "Enough, enough!" The daughters-in-law stopped dancing.

The ball was over. Prince Ivan went home first, found his wife's skin somewhere, took it and burned it. She arrived, looked for the skin, but it was gone, burned. She lay down to sleep with Prince Ivan, but before daybreak she said to him: "If you had waited a little, I would have been yours; now only God knows when we will be together again. Farewell! Seek me beyond the thrice ninth land, in the thrice tenth kingdom!" And the princess vanished.

A year went by, and Prince Ivan longed for his wife. In the second year, he made ready for his journey, obtained his father's and mother's blessing, and left. He walked a long time and suddenly he saw a little hut standing with its front to the woods and its back to him. He said: "Little hut, little hut, stand the old way, as thy mother stood thee, with thy back to the woods and thy front to me!" The hut turned around. He entered. An old woman was sitting there, who said: "Fie, fie! Of a Russian bone not a sound was heard, not a glimpse was seen, and now a Russian bone has come to my house of its own free will. Whither goest thou, Prince Ivan?" "First of all, old woman, give me to eat and to drink, then ask me questions." The old woman gave him to eat and to drink and put him to bed. Prince Ivan said to her: "Little grandmother, I have set out to find Elena the Fair." "Oh, my child, how long you have been away! At the beginning she often remembered thee, but now she no longer remembers thee, and has not come to see me for a long time. Go now to my middle sister, she knows more than I do."

In the morning Prince Ivan set out, came to a hut, and said: "Little hut, little hut, stand the old way, as thy mother stood thee, with thy back to the woods and thy front to me." The hut turned around. He entered, and saw an old woman sitting there, who said: "Fie, fie! Of a Russian bone not a sound was heard, not a glimpse was seen, and now a Russian bone has come to my house of its own free will. Whither goest thou, Prince Ivan?" "To get Elena the Fair, little grandmother." "Oh, Prince Ivan," said

Russia

the old woman, "thou hast been long a-coming! She has begun to forget thee, she is marrying someone else; the wedding will take place soon! She is now living with my eldest sister. Go there, but be careful. When thou approachest their house, they will sense it; Elena will turn into a spindle, and her dress will turn into gold thread. My sister will wind the gold thread; when she has wound it around the spindle, and put it into a box and locked the box, thou must find the key, open the box, break the spindle, throw the top of it in back of thee, and the bottom of it in front of thee. Then she will appear before thee."

Prince Ivan went, came to the third old woman's house, and entered. The old woman was winding gold thread; she wound it around the spindle and put it in a box, locked the box, and put the key somewhere. He took the key, opened the box, took out the spindle, broke it just as he had been told, cast the top in back of him and the bottom in front of him. Suddenly Elena the Fair stood before him and greeted him: "Oh, you have been a long time coming, Prince Ivan! I almost married someone else." And she told him that the other bridegroom was expected soon. Elena the Fair took a magic carpet from the old woman, sat on it with Prince Ivan, and they took off and flew like birds. The other bridegroom suddenly arrived and learned that they had left. He too was cunning! He began to pursue them, and chased and chased them, and came within ten yards of overtaking them: but on their carpet they flew into Russia, and for some reason he could not get into Russia, so he turned back. The happy bride and groom came home; everyone rejoiced, and soon Ivan and Elena began to live and prosper, for the glory of all the people.

The Frog Princess

145

QUESTIONS FOR DISCUSSION

1. Do you detect similar ideas behind these tales? Of course, in each case someone is transformed from an animal into human form. But beyond this, note what the redemption of the bewitched human depends upon, in each story. Is there any similarity here? Explain.
2. Compare the circumstances of Prince Ivan and the merchant's daughter. Why do you think so many folktales concern the rich and powerful, when they were, after all, the tales of the common people?
3. The girl had called the dog "sweet-as-a-honeycomb" on numerous occasions, but nothing happened as a result of her kind words until the last incident. What, then, do you think, was the real test that turned the dog into a handsome man? Is this type of test present in the Russian version? What bearing does such action have on the form of the folktale?
4. In "The Frog Princess," when all seems won, victory fades, and Prince Ivan has to begin all over again. Diagram the incidents in the narrative to show the underlying pattern. Note that the action rises, falls, then rises again sharply.

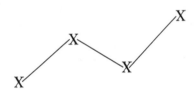

5. These tales are told from the third person point of view. Through which characters, however, do we see the action develop in each of the stories? Would the story be different if, say, in "The Frog Princess," the frog had told the story? Would it have been as satisfactory? Why, or why not?
6. The basic motif in these tales involves contrast—the beauty and the beast. "The Small-Tooth Dog" contrasts the devotion of the dog and the disgust of the girl, for example. What other contrasts are noticeable? Discuss.

SUGGESTIONS FOR COMPOSITION

1. Create your own Beauty and the Beast folktale. Put the characters and incidents into a modern setting, but keep the elements of magic and enchantment.
2. Are folktales *true*? Write a short composition in which you discuss the various meanings of this word and show that folktales are both true and not true.

THE UGLY DUCKLING MOTIF

Do you ever daydream? It is a pleasant and rather common diversion. Folktales are often defined as the universal daydreams of mankind. Of all the daydreams people have delighted in, none have ever been more popular than those in which the clever and conceited are outwitted. To make the outwitting even more satisfactory, it helps if a stupid fellow does it. Many tales tell of a ridiculed person who triumphs over his tormentors. One such story is the classic tale of the ugly duckling which turns into a beautiful swan.

Here are two more stories of the same sort—one German, the other Russian.

Hans, unlike his clever brother, set out on his mission to find and free the lovely princess, without either a horse or his father's blessing. Hans carried along one thing on his quest, however, which his older brother did not possess, and this was to be the dragons' undoing. A great many of you also possess this valuable item. Can you guess what it is?

The Enchanted Princess

Once there was a poor craftsman who had two sons. One was nice and the other horrid, but as sometimes happens in this peculiar world, the father loved the nasty one, whose name was Helmrich, more than the nice one, who was called Hans.

The years passed and a time came when the craftsman found that he had been paying out more money than people had been paying him and that his purse was quite empty. I must do something about this, the poor man thought. If my customers will not come to me to pay their bills, I must go to them and ask for my money. It is up to me. I must be polite, but firm. So off he went early each morning, knocking at people's doors. But the grandest people are not always the best payers, and no one likes paying bills, and day after day the poor man returned home tired and with his purse as empty as when he had set out. He could not bear to go home and see his wife's long face and worried expression, so he would sit outside the door of the inn, sad and lonely, and not in the mood—even had it been possible—to go inside and join the others.

However, though he sat there by himself, busy with his own gloomy thoughts, he could not help hearing what the others were saying inside. One day he heard a stranger who had just come from the big city, telling some story. At first he listened with only half an ear, then with a whole ear, and finally with both ears, for what the stranger was telling them was that the king's lovely young daughter had been placed under a spell and made captive by a wicked witch and must remain in her prison till someone came who could pass three tests. If anyone did come and managed to pass these difficult tests, the king had promised that he should have the lovely princess' hand, the magnificent castle and all the things in it.

When he heard this, the craftsman thought to himself, my son Helmrich is a smart young chap. He could shave a billy goat's beard, if anyone asked him to, and I'm sure he could pass those tests. Then he would marry the lovely princess and become lord of the land and all its people, and all my troubles would be over.

So, forgetting all about his sorrows and the money people owed him, he hurried home to tell his wife the news. The next morning he told

his son Helmrich about it, and Helmrich said that he would try his luck,
so his father fitted him out with a horse, sword, pistols and fine clothes, just
as quickly as possible. As he set out, Helmrich promised that he would soon
come in a coach with six horses to fetch them and his stupid brother Hans.
He already felt as though he were king.

    Helmrich was rather a high-spirited, spiteful youth, and he vented
his spite in a very nasty way on all the creatures he met. He threw sticks
and stones at the birds singing their songs in praise of Our Lord, and
frightened them off their branches. He never came across an animal without scaring it or playing some trick on it. When he saw an ant heap, he
rode his horse at it and made him trample it; then, when the angry ants
climbed onto his horse and him, he squashed and killed them all. A little
later he came to a pond on which twelve ducks were swimming. He lured
these onto the bank and killed them all but one, which managed to escape.
Then he came upon a hive of wild bees and destroyed it, as he had done
the ant heap. His greatest pleasure was not to protect innocent creatures,
but to torment and destroy them out of sheer spitefulness and nastiness.

In the evening as the sun was going down he reached the splendid castle in which the enchanted princess was imprisoned. He knocked loudly on the castle gate. There was no reply. Then he banged more loudly still on the great gate, and in the end a little shutter in the gate opened and an aged, wizened old crone with a face the color of cobwebs looked out and crossly asked what he wanted.

"I've come to free the princess," Helmrich said. "Open up, go on, hurry up!"

"Not so fast, young fellow, tomorrow will do. I shall expect you here at nine o'clock." Then the shutter was closed again and the old crone was gone.

The next morning at nine o'clock the old woman was standing waiting outside the gate. When she saw Helmrich coming, she scattered a jugful of linseed over a stretch of grass and said, "Pick up all the seeds. I shall come back in an hour, and you must have finished by then."

Helmrich thought that a very bad joke, and certainly he was not going to break his back picking up all those seeds, so he went for a stroll instead. As a result, when the old woman came back, she found the jug empty.

"This is bad," she said, with a grave face. Then she took twelve little golden bowls from her pocket and threw them into the castle pond. "Get those bowls out. I shall be back in an hour, and you must be finished by then."

Helmrich just laughed, shrugged his shoulders, and went for another stroll.

When the old woman came back and found that he had not done that task either, she called out twice: "This is bad, bad." Then she took Helmrich by the hand and led him through the gate and across the courtyard and into the great hall of the castle. There sat three figures enveloped in thick white veils.

"Choose, my son, but choose correctly! I shall be back in an hour."

When the old woman returned, Helmrich was still no wiser and had no idea which to choose, so he chose at random.

"I choose the one on the right."

Then all three threw back their veils. The one sitting in the middle was the princess. Right and left of her sat two horrible dragons. One of the dragons seized Helmrich in its curly, long talons and threw him through the window into a deep abyss.

A year had passed since Helmrich had left home to rescue the lovely princess, and still his parents waited for him to come driving up in a coach with six spanking horses. In the end they could only believe that some dreadful accident had happened to their son.

"Ah," wailed the unhappy father, "if only clumsy Hans had gone instead of our bright lad, it would not have been so bad."

"Father," said Hans, "let me go too. Please, I would like to try, and I must find out what has happened to my brother."

But the father would not hear of it. He asked himself what chance his clumsy, stupid son would have if his clever, bright one had not succeeded. So, he refused to let Hans have either a horse or weapons.

Hans, however, decided that he would do without, but go he would. So he set off secretly and walked along the road for three days till he came to the castle. He was not in the least afraid. At night he slept on soft green moss at the feet of tall old trees and slept as well and as soundly as he did at home. Nor were the birds of the forest frightened of him. On the contrary, they came and sang him their loveliest songs. When he passed the ant heap that his brother had destroyed, he saw the ants still busy repairing the last of the damage. He even bent down and tried to help them, and those that by mistake crawled up onto him, he carefully picked off and set down on the ground without hurting them. When he came to the pond, he called the ducks to the bank and shared the remains of his bread with them. And when he saw the bees, he plucked some flowers and laid them by the entrance to the hive.

Then, happy at being alive, he reached the old castle and knocked shyly on the gate. The shutter opened, and the old woman asked him what he wanted.

"If I am not too humble a person," said Hans, "I would very much like to try and rescue the beautiful princess."

At once the great gate was opened and the old woman said, "Try my son, by all means, but remember that if you cannot pass the three tests, it will cost you your life."

"Never mind, mother, I would like to try," said Hans.

Then the old woman put him to the first test, scattering the linseed and telling him that she would be back in an hour, by which time he must have finished. Hans was not lazy. He bent down and began working feverishly, but, as it seemed, in almost no time at all the three-quarters had struck and the bottom of the jug was little more than covered. Hans was on the point of despairing, when two ants came crawling up, then more and more, and in a moment the ground was black with them. Each picked up a seed, and in a moment or two the jug was full. There was not one linseed left anywhere on the grass.

When the old woman saw this, she said, "Good. That is good." Then she threw the twelve bowls into the pond. Hans at once plunged into the depths to try and fish the bowls up in time. Yet, however deep he dived, he could never reach the bottom. Desperate, he sat down on the bank and wondered what on earth he could do. Then, looking up, he saw twelve ducklings come swimming up and each held one of the golden bowls in its beak. They came out of the water and laid the bowls on the grass. And so Hans' second task was completed in time.

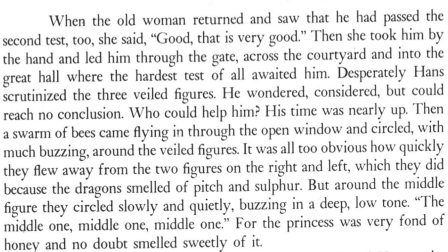

When the old woman returned and saw that he had passed the second test, too, she said, "Good, that is very good." Then she took him by the hand and led him through the gate, across the courtyard and into the great hall where the hardest test of all awaited him. Desperately Hans scrutinized the three veiled figures. He wondered, considered, but could reach no conclusion. Who could help him? His time was nearly up. Then a swarm of bees came flying in through the open window and circled, with much buzzing, around the veiled figures. It was all too obvious how quickly they flew away from the two figures on the right and left, which they did because the dragons smelled of pitch and sulphur. But around the middle figure they circled slowly and quietly, buzzing in a deep, low tone. "The middle one, middle one, middle one." For the princess was very fond of honey and no doubt smelled sweetly of it.

At the end of the hour the old woman returned, and Hans, quite sure and decided in his own mind, pointed to the middle figure and said, "That is the king's daughter." At that the evil dragons shot through the window at lightning speed and were never seen again. The lovely princess then threw off her veil, rejoicing at being free and pleased to be Hans' bride.

Hans hastened to have the fastest coach in the castle harnessed with a team of six horses, and sent it to fetch his parents, and they all lived happily and free from care to the end of their days.

The Enchanted Princess

153

Context Clues

In paragraph 7 you will find the phrase "wizened old crone." From the other details given in the same paragraph, what do you think this phrase means?

Can you infer the meaning of "the three-quarters had struck" (page 320) from the rest of the paragraph?

"Desperately Hans *scrutinized* the three veiled figures." Give a synonym for the italicized word.

Making New Verbs: -ize

When a new word is coined and we want to give it a verb form, we often add *-ize*, a very useful verb ending. For example, when Louis Pasteur discovered how to make milk safe to drink, the process was named for him. We *pasteurize* milk. Later, when we learned how to stop the cream from separating from the milk when it stands, the process was called *homogenizing*. Can you tell why? When we influence other countries to do things the way we do, we say we have *Americanized* them. Can you think of other new words that have been made in this way with *-ize*?

Poor Ivan! He has many troubles, but he proves that the world does not belong only to the clever. This Russian tale is told with tongue-in-cheek, and the narrator seems to enjoy the telling as much as he expects his listeners to.

Ivan The Simpleton

In a certain land, in a certain kingdom, there lived an old man and his old wife. They had three sons, of whom the third was called Ivan the Simpleton. The first two sons were married, but Ivan the Simpleton was a bachelor. The first two were busy: they managed the house, plowed, and sowed, but the third did nothing at all. One day the old father and his daughters-in-law sent Ivan to finish plowing a few rods of land. The young boy came to the field, harnessed his horse, drove once or twice over the field with his plow, and saw countless swarms of mosquitoes and midges. He grabbed a whip, lashed one side of his horse, and killed a host of these bugs;

he lashed the other side of his horse and killed forty gadflies. He thought to himself: "Here with one stroke I have killed forty mighty knights and a countless host of lesser warriors!" He gathered them all together, put them in a pile, and covered them with horse dung; he did not continue plowing, but unharnessed his horse and drove home. Upon his return he said to his sisters-in-law and his mother: "Give me a piece of thick cloth and a saddle, and you, father, give me the rusty saber that hangs on the wall. I am not a real peasant, I have no land!"

His family laughed at him, and to mock him gave him a cracked clod instead of a saddle; our fellow attached girths to it and laid it across a wretched mare. Instead of a piece of thick cloth, his mother gave him a ragged old dress of hers; he took this, sharpened his father's saber, made ready for his journey, and left. He came to a crossroads, and since he knew how to write a little, he wrote on the guidepost: "Let the mighty Ilya Muromets and Fyodor Lyzhnikov come to such and such a kingdom to see the strong and mighty hero who in one stroke killed forty mighty knights and an unnumbered host of lesser warriors, and covered them all with a stone."

Soon after him, Ilya Muromets came to the same crossroads and read the inscription on the post. "Ha!" he said. "A strong and mighty hero has passed by here; it is not meet to disobey him." He rode on and overtook Vaniukha, and while he was still at a distance, doffed his cap and saluted him: "Good day, strong and mighty hero!" Vaniukha did not doff his cap, and said: "Good day, Iliukha!" They rode together. After a short time Fyodor Lyzhnikov came to the same post, read the inscription, and decided that he too should heed the summons—after all, Ilya Muromets had heeded it! So he rode in the same direction; while he was still at a distance he doffed his cap and said: "Good day, strong and mighty hero!" But Vaniukha did not doff his cap, and said: "Good day, Fediunka!"

All three of them rode together; they came to a certain kingdom, and stopped in the royal meadows. The heroes pitched their tents, and Vaniukha spread his old dress; the two heroes tied their steeds with silken ropes, but Vaniukha broke a twig from a tree, twisted it, and tied his mare with it. And so they settled themselves. From his castle the king saw that strangers were foraging in his meadows and at once sent one of his familiars to find out who they were. He came to the meadows, approached Ilya Muromets, and asked him what manner of men they were and why they thus trampled the king's meadows without permission. Ilya Muromets answered: "It is not for me to answer! Ask our chief, the strong and mighty hero."

The envoy approached Vaniukha, who began to shout at him before he could utter a word: "Get away while you still can, and tell the

156

king that in his meadows there is a strong and mighty hero who in one stroke killed forty mighty knights and an unnumbered host of lesser warriors and covered them with a stone—and that Ilya Muromets and Fyodor Lyzhnikov are with him, and that he demands the king's daughter in marriage!" The envoy conveyed this message to the king. The king consulted the annals: Ilya Muromets and Fyodor Lyzhnikov were mentioned there, but the third one, who in one stroke had killed forty knights, was not. Then the king ordered his army to gather, seize the three knights, and bring them before him. But this was no easy task! When Vaniukha saw the army approaching he cried: "Ilyukha, drive away this rabble!" And he himself lay down, stretched out, and watched the scene like an owl.

At his command Ilya Muromets jumped on his steed, galloped forward, and did not so much smite with his hands as trample with his steed; he knocked down the whole army, leaving only a few messengers to inform the king of what had happened. Upon hearing the news of the disaster, the king assembled even greater forces and sent them to seize the three knights. Ivan the Simpleton cried: "Fediunka, drive away this scum!" Fyodor jumped on his steed and knocked them all down, leaving only a few messengers.

What could the king do? He was in sore straits; the three knights had defeated his army. He began to cudgel his brains, and recalled that in his kingdom there lived a strong hero, Dobrynya. He sent him a letter, asking him to come to the royal meadows and conquer the three knights. Dobrynya came; the king received him on his third-story balcony, and Dobrynya on horseback was level with the king on the balcony—so mighty was he! He saluted the king and they spoke together. Then he went to the king's meadows. Ilya Muromets and Fyodor Lyzhnikov saw Dobrynya riding toward them, became frightened, jumped on their steeds, and made away. But Vaniukha had no time to run away, for while he got his mare ready, Dobrynya approached him and began to laugh at the sight of this vaunted hero—he was so short and so thin! Dobrynya bent his head down level with Vaniukha's face and stared at him in amusement. Vaniukha did not lose his presence of mind; he drew out his saber and cut off Dobrynya's head.

The king saw this and was frightened. "Oh," he said, "the knight has slain Dobrynya. Now we are indeed in trouble! Go quickly, call the hero to my palace." Such a brilliant delegation came to fetch Vaniukha that, Lord save us, the very best carriages and people of the highest rank were there. They seated him in a coach and brought him before the king. The king received him hospitably and gave him his daughter in marriage; they celebrated their wedding, and are still alive to this very day and chewing bread.

I was at their wedding and drank mead; it ran down my mustache but did not go into my mouth. I asked for a cap, and received a slap; I was given a robe, and on my way home a titmouse flew over me cackling: "Flowing robe!" I thought she was saying, "Throw away the robe," and threw it away. This is not the tale, but a flourish, for fun. The tale itself has not begun!

QUESTIONS FOR DISCUSSION

1. Point of view plays an important part in the Ugly Duckling stories, since the point of view or attitude of one character toward another actually sets the tale in motion and develops the subject. Note the importance of point of view in "Ivan the Simpleton." Why did Ivan's two mighty heroes travel with him and help him? What was their attitude toward him? Why didn't the army immediately attack the three trespassers? Actually, the whole tale rests on a misunderstanding which creates a false viewpoint. Explain.

2. It is, of course, Ivan's attitude toward his own strength that sets this tale in motion. What misconception caused him to leave home? How does this opening incident differ from that of "The Enchanted Princess"? Our sympathies are invited for Hans, but not for Ivan. Despite this, we take pleasure in Ivan's making fools of his two strong-armed friends and of the men who attack him. Why?

3. Humor is closely associated with point of view or attitude. Actually, all humor springs from the incongruous—that is, from the unexpected. What incongruity do you find in the situation described in the Russian tale?

4. In each of these tales the hero sets out on a quest. What does each seek? Why, in each case, did the hero leave home? It will help you to understand the form of the tales if you draw a diagram of each journey, noting the important incidents that occurred. What other stories have you read that employed a journey motif?

5. The Russian tale is quite different in some respects from the other tale. Do you notice any difference in the *way* the tale is told? Most folktales employ supernatural aid for their heroes. Does this one? Does the form of this story seem to differ in any other way from that of "The Enchanted Princess"?

SUGGESTIONS FOR COMPOSITION

1. Create an "Ivan the Simpleton" yourself — one who outwits the teachers, drives principals to the brink of insanity, and wins out, in blundering fashion, over his cleverer classmates. If possible, make a recording of your story, and let the class listen to it.
2. Ask the librarian to help you find some additional folktales. Perhaps you could give your classmates a quick summary of a few tales, then see if they can identify the basic subject, or motif, of each.
3. We mentioned earlier that folktales have been used by many modern writers. Some use the subjects of folktales for stories of their own. See if you can locate a story with a subject similar to that of one of the tales you've studied. Report on it to the class.
4. Many folk tales invite illustrations. If you enjoy painting or sketching, select a scene from a folktale that you think would make a particularly good illustration. Try a watercolor or perhaps a charcoal sketch.
5. Dramatize one or more of the scenes that appeal to you. With the aid of your friends, select a scene, write out the various parts (you'll need conversation), plan the setting, and present it to the class.

A SUMMING UP

1. Try making a list of some of the things you believe most people wish for. Avoid specific items, such as cars or yachts. Instead, deal with general terms, like wealth and good luck. Now think back over the folktales you have read. How many of the wishes on your list fit one or more folktale subjects? What does this tell you about folktales?
2. What are folktales about? Can you make a general statement about the subject of the folktale?
3. Consider again the characters in each tale. Do the heroes and heroines grow, change, or develop? Do the wicked remain wicked, the good remain good? What does this tell you about some of the characteristics of the folktale?
4. Discuss various stories or movies or television shows that use these folktale motifs. Why do you think they do it so often? What does this tell you about people's wishes in being entertained?
5. Which of the folktale motifs you have studied appeals the most to you? Try writing a short folktale with that motif or pattern. Use some of the characteristics of the folktale that you have discovered in your reading. If possible, have the class read your story and decide whether you have followed the pattern well enough to have developed a recognizable folktale.

Arnott, Kathleen, *African Myths and Legends*, ill. by Jean Kiddell-Monroe. Walch, 1963.

Belting, Natalia M., *The Long-Tailed Bear and Other Indian Legends*, ill. by Louis F. Cary. Bobbs-Merrill, 1961. (This volume contains tales from 22 tribes.)

Botkin, Ben and Carl Withers, *The Illustrated book of American Folklore*. Grosset & Dunlap, 1958.

Colum, Padraic, ed., *The Arabian Nights: Tales of Wonder and Magnificence*, ill. by Lynd Ward. The Macmillan Co., 1953.

Courlander, Harold, *The King's Drum and Other Stories*, ill. by Enrico Arns. Harcourt Brace Jovanovich, 1962. (This contains 30 African folktales whose various motifs will be familiar.)

Downing, Charles, *Russian Tales and Legends*, ill. by Joan Kiddell-Monroe. Oxford University Press, 1957.

Grimm, Jacob and Wilhelm Grimm, *Grimm's Fairy Tales*, complete edition, ill. by Joseph Schnarl. Pantheon Books, 1944.

Jacobs, Joseph, *Celtic Fairy Tales*, ill. by John Batten. G. P. Putnam's Sons, 1892.
———, *English Fairy Tales*. G. P. Putnam's Sons, 1892.

Jones, Gwyn, *Scandinavian Legends and Folk Tales*, ill. by Joan Kiddell-Monroe. Walch, 1956.

Lim, Sian-Teki, *Folk Tales From China*, ill. by William Arthur Smith. The John Day Company, 1944.

Macmanus, Seumas, *The Bold Heroes of Hungry Hill and Other Irish Folk Tales*, ill. by Jay Chollick. Ariel Books, 1951.

Picard, Barbara Leonie, *German Hero Sagas and Folk Tales*, ill. by Joan Kiddell-Monroe. Walch, 1958.

Robinson, W. Heath, *Perrault's Complete Fairy Tales*, ill. by W. Heath Robinson. Dodd, Mead & Co., 1961.

Wheeler, Post, *Russian Wonder Tales*. Thomas Yoseloff, 1957. (This contains twelve of the famous Bilibin illustrations in color, together with sixteen tales.)

ABOUT THE AUTHORS

Aesop (late 6th century B.C.) *Greek fabulist*
You can tell from the fables you have read that this Greek storyteller was indeed a witty fellow. But if we composed a moral for the little we know of Aesop's own life, it would probably read, "Be tactful in exposing the foibles of men of great influence." Had Aesop heeded that advice, his life perhaps would not have ended so abruptly. On one of his missions as emissary for the wealthy King Croesus, his wit offended the priests at the Temple of Delphi, the home of an ancient Greek oracle, and they tossed him over a cliff to his death. His fables have survived for these many centuries because of their appeal to all men.

Olivia Coolidge (1908–   ) *English teacher, historian*
Olivia Coolidge, the daughter of a historian and journalist, graduated from Oxford University in England and has taught school in Germany, England, and the United States. She has been especially interested in mythology and has written versions of both Greek and Norse myths for young people.

Ivan Andreevich Krilof (1769–1844) *Russian fabulist*
To survive in a poor family in Russia during the eighteenth century demanded a sharp power of observation, a keenness of wit, and a driving ambition. Ivan Krilof developed these attributes at an early age. At nine years of age he labored as a clerk to bring home money. At thirteen he wrote his first work, a comic opera in verse. Soon a number of his works were published. He often lashed out at the foolishness and dishonesty of public officials. The government was angered by these attacks, and by the time he was twenty-four had refused to allow any of his writings to be printed. The next ten years found Ivan Krilof drifting through Russia. In his spare time he translated some French fables into Russian, and they pleased him so much that he began to write some fables of his own. When these were finally published, the government reversed its attitude and bestowed upon the author a position in a public library. Krilof dedicated himself to the fable and wrote nine volumes of them before his death. They have been very popular throughout the world.

Lin Yutang (1895–   ) *Chinese-American essayist, translator*
Born in the tiny mountain village of Changchow, Amoy, in China, Lin Yutang knows the Chinese people as only a native Chinese can. But with his education in Germany and the United States as well as China, he has been able to share his knowledge with people in other lands. He has translated and interpreted countless Chinese tales and has edited many collections of Chinese literature. He has worked with the United Nations and has also been a college teacher in the United States.

i

James Thurber (1894–1961) *American humorist, illustrator*

Not even the threat of total blindness halted the work of this remarkable writer. As his eyesight dimmed in his last years, he used huge yellow sheets of paper on which to scrawl out his manuscripts. Eventually, he found it easier to "write" and revise in his head, and then dictate the entire finished work for someone else to write down. Thurber felt that people laughed at his stories because they saw their own faces in them, and their own silliness, and were touched with amusement and relief. Certainly he specialized in tickling human confusion into laughter, as you can see in his fable "The Owl Who Was God." Frequently he illustrated his own works with zany cartoons; you can find some of the best of them in *The Seal in the Bedroom* (1931) and *The Owl in the Attic* (1932).

Index of Authors and Titles

Index

iv

Illustration Credits

v

Illustration Credits